D0442145

AN APOLOGY

for the life of

Mrs. SHAMELA Andrews

An APOLOGY for the LIFE of MRS. SHAMELA ANDREWS

BY HENRY FIELDING

Edited, with an Introduction and Notes by
SHERIDAN W. BAKER, JR.

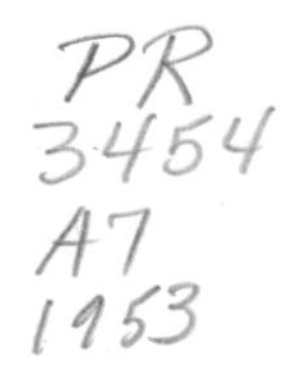

UNIVERSITY OF CALIFORNIA PRESS
Berkeley and Los Angeles, 1953

University of California Press
Berkeley and Los Angeles
Cambridge University Press
London, England

Printed in the United States of America
Designed and illustrated by Rita Carroll

TO

BERTRAND H. BRONSON

ACKNOWLEDGMENTS

I AM *deeply indebted to the Faculty Research Fund of The Horace Rackham School of Graduate Studies, University of Michigan; to the librarians of Yale University, the University of Illinois, and the Huntington Library; to Margaret I. Smith and the reference staff of the University of Michigan Library; and to Professors Louis I. Bredvold, Arthur E. Hutson, and Henry V. S. Ogden.*

S.W.B.

Ann Arbor, Michigan

CONTENTS

INTRODUCTION

PREVIOUS EDITIONS of Henry Fielding's *Shamela* are not to be bought. The two editions and Dublin printing of 1741 are rare books, and the modern editions of R. Brimley Johnson (1926) and of Brian W. Downs (1930) are almost equally out of reach. The present edition therefore intends to fill a need among readers of Fielding and readers of Samuel Richardson—against whom Fielding struck his spark—and among all those who like books. *Shamela* is not only a little book of great historical interest; it is not only a work which turned Henry Fielding from a minor dramatist and journalist into a major novelist: it is itself a masterpiece. It may well be the best parody in English literature.

In the history of the novel, *Shamela* holds a highly distinguished place, standing as it does between the two books which are alternately taken to be the first modern English novel: between Richardson's *Pamela* and Fielding's *Joseph Andrews.* The history of the modern novel may conveniently be said to begin when Richardson anonymously published his *Pamela: Or, Virtue Rewarded* on November 6, 1740. By April 4, 1741, the tremendous popularity of these adventures of Pamela Andrews had drawn out Fielding's *An Apology for the Life of Mrs. Shamela Andrews,* ridiculing as sham the self-centered virtue of Richardson's heroine. A kind of collision between the masculine temperament of Fielding and the feminine temperament of Richardson produced this impudent child, in whom the features of both parents are simultaneously and comically visible, features which appear again transfigured in Fielding's *Joseph Andrews* of the following year. The parodist had become a novelist. Springing from the Richardsonian novel—the novel of emotional analysis, of tender hopes and fears, the novel which sees life as potentially tragic—*Shamela* brought forth the novel of manners, of panoramic social criticism, the novel which sees life as comic.

I

But Fielding never acknowledged *Shamela* as his. Moreover, Fielding's friend Arthur Murphy ignored *Shamela* when he made the first edition of Fielding's works and wrote the first Fielding biography in 1762. *Shamela* is recognized in no subsequent edition of Fielding's works, nor mentioned by a single one of Fielding's nineteenth-century admirers. Nevertheless, we can no longer doubt that Fielding wrote it.

Evidence for Fielding's authorship begins to appear in 1883 when Austin Dobson and Leslie Stephen, writing on Fielding and Richardson respectively, both quote from a letter in which Richardson refers to *Shamela* as Fielding's, and both omit any mention of *Shamela* whatsoever. In 1900 Clara L. Thomson quotes Richardson's statement (her attention perhaps called to it by Stephen's preface) and makes a brief for Fielding's authorship, noting that Richardson's Mr. B. is named Mr. Booby in *Shamela* and

Joseph Andrews alike. In 1901 Ethel M. M. McKenna's reference to *Shamela* as Fielding's "famous parody" brings Austin Dobson grumbling from his study. "A discussion has lately arisen as to the authorship of this *Apology,* which has attracted to it more attention than it has hitherto received or deserves," he tells us in his *Samuel Richardson* (1902). But on another of Richardson's letters Dobson has had the misfortune of finding a marginal note in Richardson's hand again assigning *Shamela* to Fielding. Moreover, Dobson admits, inside the book and out, other evidence points to Fielding. Mrs. Slipslop of *Joseph Andrews* uses the malapropisms of Shamela and Mrs. Jewkes. A Parson Oliver appears in *Shamela;* Fielding's boyhood tutor was a Parson Oliver (not to mention the play upon "Mister Oliver" which becomes "Trulliber" in *Joseph Andrews*). Dodd publishes *Shamela;* Dodd has published before and will publish again for Fielding. Finally, *Shamela* fits exactly into the pattern of Fielding's running feud with Colley Cibber, former manager of Drury Lane Theater and Poet Laureate of England. Anyway, says Dobson, no one has the right to call *Shamela* Fielding's "famous parody."

But Dobson was to turn up still a third reference to Fielding as author of *Shamela,* a letter by one Thomas Dampier, and Dobson's successors have continued to find argument and stylistic evidence for Fielding's authorship. Professor Charles B. Woods offers, in a recent article, a bibliography and further persuasion.[1] The most recent

[1] "Fielding and the Authorship of Shamela," *The Philological Quarterly,* XXV (1948).

concrete evidence was added in 1936 by Professor Alan D. McKillop:[2] a catalogue of a bankruptcy sale on July 10, 1746, in which the half interest of bookseller Francis Cogan in "Shamela, by Fielding" was sold to Andrew Millar, Fielding's friend, the publisher of his major novels.

Even Fielding's silence as to *Shamela* finds plausible explanation. Indeed, he would perhaps have disowned it if he could. The Richardson who was nameless to him when he burlesqued *Pamela* was already the neighbor and friend of Fielding's four sisters, and that friendship grew. By 1748 Fielding himself praises Richardson's new *Clarissa.* As R. Brimley Johnson has observed, Fielding quite probably would not care further to disturb his great rival with a public confession of what was already known: that he had written *Shamela.*

Since Dobson, no one who has considered the problem has doubted for more than a scholarly minute that the book is Fielding's. No one has ever so much as suggested another author for it. And even if some back cupboard eventually produces another claimant, the possibility of explaining away all the evidence that points to Fielding seems indeed remote. Perhaps the only rebuttal possible is to challenge as over-facile some of the parallels between *Shamela* and acknowledged works of Fielding. Wilbur L. Cross,[3] for example, makes the point that Shamela "has Parson Adams's habit of snapping her fingers." But

---

[2] *Samuel Richardson, Printer and Novelist* (Chapel Hill, University of North Carolina Press, 1936), p. 74.

[3] *The History of Henry Fielding,* 3 vols. (New Haven, Yale University Press, 1918), I, 307.

Shamela snaps her fingers in deliberate contempt; Adams unconsciously, when excited. Certain similarities in phrasing also lose strength when we look outside Fielding's works. Perhaps making Shamela the "lady" instead of the "wife" of the hero, just as in *Joseph Andrews,* is characteristic of Fielding.[4] But any writer of *Shamela* would perhaps have used the same term, if not from his own word stock, then from the *Pamela* he is mimicking: ". . . if you make Mrs. *Andrews* your Lady, she will do Credit to your Choice." Similarly, although Fielding liked to ridicule the publisher's phrase "Necessary to be had in all FAMILIES," its appearance on the title page of *Shamela* may go no further than direct burlesque of the prediction made in the first letter introductory to *Pamela:* ". . . it will be found worthy a Place, . . . in all Families." The same may be said for Paul de Castro's discovery that Fielding uses the phrase "be not righteous over much" in *The Champion* and that Shamela hears Parson Williams preach a sermon on the text *Be not Righteous over-much.* The advice to "Be not righteous over much" is found also in the fifth of the letters prefixed to *Pamela.* But this leads us to Fielding's characteristic absorption of current phrases and attitudes, and to the timeliness upon which burlesque feeds. All in all, the conclusion that Fielding wrote *Shamela* is inescapable.

II

The timeliness of *Shamela* is inseparable from several of Fielding's basic concerns. In addition to *Pamela,* three

[4] *Ibid.*

current books give point to *Shamela: A Short Account of God's Dealings with the Reverend Mr. George Whitefield* (1740), *An Apology for the Life of Mr. Colley Cibber, Comedian* (1740), and Conyers Middleton's *Life of Cicero* (1741—two months before *Shamela*).[5] As live game for burlesque each stirred Fielding in its own way.

At a glance, the several references in *Shamela* to Whitefield's *Short Account of God's Dealings* would seem merely to satirize Pamela's piety and book learning. The prominence of Parson Williams also doubtless owes much to the simple exaggeration of Pamela's acquaintance with that young man. But when Fielding gives Williams a sermon on the text "be not righteous overmuch," we realize that Williams is drawn together from the dust of a popular turmoil, and shaped by ideas that had been turning in Fielding's head as well. Williams's sermon takes its title from a series of four preached in April and May, 1739, by Dr. Joseph Trapp against the Methodist George Whitefield, himself present in the congregation during the

[5] Fielding alludes to other current books. Professor Charles B. Woods identifies: (1) *A full Answer is a plain and true Account*, an answer to Bishop Benjamin Hoadly's *A Plain Account of the Nature and End of the Sacrament*, admired by Parson Adams in *Joseph Andrews;* (2) *Orpheus and Eurydice*, a pantomime by Lewis Theobald ridiculed by Fielding in *The Champion;* (3) *Venus in the Cloyster; or, the Nun in her Smock*, a pornographic booklet which brought publisher Edmund Curll to trial. Better known are the Earl of Rochester's notoriously bawdy *Poems;* Mrs. Mary Manley's *New Atalantis*, a collection of current scandals disguised as incidents in a romantic tale; and *The Whole Duty of Man*, a favorite household book of devotion.

first sermon. *The Nature, Folly, Sin, and Danger of being Righteous over-much,* a text from Ecclesiastes, went through several editions before the end of the year. *The Gentleman's Magazine* for June printed a long extract, slightly edited so as to begin with the words "To be righteous over-much." The phrase obviously was in the air, as was the controversy, kept aloft by Whitefield's *Dealings* in 1740, and by replies to Trapp from Whitefield, Seagrave, Law, and others. The same page of *The Gentleman's Magazine*[6] which announces the arrival of *Shamela* lists "Dr. *Trapp*'s reply to Mr. *Law*."

But in Williams Fielding comprehends both sides of the controversy. He is by nature disposed toward the popular side—its popularity by no means a deterrent—the side of temperance against enthusiasm, of reason against inspiration, of Established Church against Methodist innovation. Consequently into Williams go all the popular accusations against Whitefield and the Methodists: that the Methodists claimed a special Grace which exempted them from good works, made them arrogant and hypocritical, freed them to sin with their bodies since salvation of their souls had been guaranteed. Hence the casuistry and licentiousness of Williams and the enthusiasm for grace and pleasant emotions of Tickletext.

Actually both Tickletext and Fielding's anti-Methodism had already begun to form in *The Author's Farce* (1730), Fielding's first broad satire. Of course, the several young men talking together in their rooms at Oxford had yet attracted neither wide attention nor the name of Meth-

[6] *Op. cit.* (April, 1741), p. 224.

odists, and Fielding must look toward Scotland for his dissident and comic clergyman. But Mr. Murder-text, the Presbyterian Parson, speaks—though briefly—the language of Tickletext and Williams. A pretty girl asks that the company may dance. Says Murder-text:

Verily, I am conquer'd—Pity prevaileth over Severity, and the Flesh hath subdued the Spirit—I feel a motion in me, and whether it be of Grace or no I am not certain—Pretty Maid, I cannot be deaf any longer to your Prayers, I will abide the performing of a Dance, . . . being thereto mov'd by an inward working. . . .

And in *The Grub-Street Opera* (1731) Parson Puzzletext[7] exploits this same rhetorical cassock. *Shamela* simply formulates as anti-Methodism Fielding's previous criticisms of pious hypocrisy, and Fielding continues to repeat the formula throughout his subsequent works. All will recall Thwackum of *Tom Jones,* who propounds the doctrine of grace and accuses Allworthy of "being righteous overmuch."

[7] Parsons Oliver and Tickletext both may ultimately derive their names from Shakespeare's Parson Oliver Martext, with perhaps another textual parson assisting. In Christopher Bullock's *Woman's Revenge: or, a Match in Newgate* (revived in 1728 in the wake of *The Beggar's Opera* and acted twenty times during Fielding's theater years) a Parson Tickletext is mentioned by a malapropist not unlike Mrs. Jewkes or Mrs. Slipslop. But whatever Fielding's immediate source, we can see more than accident in the progression: Martext—Murdertext (together with a Marplay in *The Author's Farce*)—Puzzletext—Tickletext. And "Tickletext" might have suggested "Oliver," a choice endorsed by Fielding's memory of Parson Oliver, his boyhood tutor.

In *The Champion* Fielding had twice cautioned himself against "being righteous over-much" and had once reprimanded Whitefield for being so (April 5 and May 24, 1740), using the phrase as Trapp does to uphold moderate, established religion. But in the mouths of Established Churchmen Williams and Thwackum the phrase shows up those pastors who would put a comfortable limit on their own righteousness. The sword cuts both ways. Although Fielding deplored Whitefield's irregular zeal, he also deplored the laxity and fatness of the clergy against which Whitefield's zeal was directed. In Puzzletext Fielding had pictured a great deal more than sanctimoniousness; he had pictured the pipe-smoking, ale-drinking, hare-hunting, time-serving country parson, the Latin scholar and politician, who was to reappear first as Williams, then variously as Trulliber, Supple, Thwackum, and indeed—transformed—as Adams himself. If the evils in both sides give us Williams, the virtues in both sides give us Adams. With John Wesley, Adams prefers a virtuous Turk to a tepid Christian;[8] he is a lovingly comic portrait of a Whitefieldian enthusiast, who nevertheless condemns Whitefield's enthusiasm:

"Sir," answered Adams, "if Mr. Whitefield had carried his doctrine no farther . . . I should have remained, as I once was, his well-wisher. I am, myself, as great an enemy to the luxury and splendor of the clergy as he can be."

Against these specific abuses of the clergy Fielding had written four essays in *The Champion* in the spring of

[8] Woods, *op. cit.*, p. 264.

1740, describing the pride and complacence and Burgundy which were eventually to go into Williams and Supple, as well as the humility and dedication which were to inspirit Adams. Professor Woods has demonstrated the agreement of Parson Oliver's closing remarks in *Shamela* with passages of religious criticism in *The Champion* and *Joseph Andrews*. Fielding's lasting concern in religious matters, together with the tempest around Whitefield, largely account for the prominence of the clergy in *Shamela*.

But a specific incident seems to have roused Fielding against both *Pamela* and the abuses of the clergy. Parson Tickletext's mention of the preaching of *Pamela* from the pulpit alludes to the actual commendation of *Pamela* from the pulpit of St. Saviour's in Southwark by Richardson's friend Dr. Benjamin Slocock. Other clergymen were not silent: Tickletext's enthusiastic letter to his friend in the country is a satirical rendering of fact. When Fielding has Tickletext write that "It is expected shortly, that his L[ordshi]p will recommend it in a [Pastoral] Letter to our whole Body," Fielding may be simply exaggerating this clerical clamor. But he may be gathering in Whitefield as well. "His Lordship" is Edmund Gibson, Bishop of London, assiduous writer of pastoral letters,[9] who himself took arms against young Whitefield on August 1, 1739, in "The Bishop of London's Pastoral Letter to the People of his Diocese; . . . by way of Caution, against Lukewarmness on one hand, and Enthusiasm on the other." Two thirds of this well-circulated letter attacked

[9] Cross, *op. cit.*, I, 311.

religious enthusiasm, with ninety quotations from Whitefield for grist. When the Editor writes of *Shamela* that "it will do more good than the *C*[*lerg*]*y* have done harm in the World," he seems to be ridiculing a remark of Pope's concerning *Pamela:* "It will do more good than many volumes of sermons." [10] Barnabas perhaps re-echoes this statement as he denounces Whitefield in *Joseph Andrews:* "Sir, the principles of . . . all the free thinkers, are not calculated to do half the mischief as those professed by this fellow and his followers."

Sandwiched between Fielding's clerical essays in *The Champion* we find his early criticisms of *An Apology for the Life of Mr. Colley Cibber.* On Saturday, March 29, 1740, Fielding prints an essay (untitled) on the clergy. The following Tuesday brings his first jab at Cibber's *Apology* (in which Cibber had characterized Fielding as a literary failure and a mudslinger). And on Saturday we find the following title before the leading essay: "THE APOLOGY FOR THE CLERGY,—*continued.*" Though Fielding is here far from burlesque, Cibber's title seems to be running in his head. Perhaps Fielding in July, 1740, had something to do with:

An Apology for the Life of Mr. T[*heophilus*] *C*[*ibber*], *Comedian. Being a Proper Sequel to the Apology for the Life of Mr. Colley Cibber, Comedian . . . Supposed to be written by Himself.*

Just as John Puff in *Shamela* recommends that the author undertake the writing of "the Life of *his Honour,*" so the

---

[10] McKillop, *op. cit.*, p. 74.

mock Theophilus Cibber (the actual name of Colley Cibber's son) in his dedication suggests his willingness to write an apology for the life of Prime Minister Robert Walpole. But there is no doubt that Fielding's political battle in *The Champion* against Walpole's government, represented by the pseudonymous Ralph Freeman in *The Daily Gazetteer,* took similar advantage of Cibber's book. On October 16, 1740, Fielding advertises:

> . . . an Apology for the Life, Actions, and Writings of RALPH FREEMAN, alias, COURT EVIL, Esq; containing an authentic History . . . during his Time. *Written by* HIMSELF.

The book is to be published by "T[heophilus] C[ibber], Publisher-General of the Ministerial Society."

Fielding's combination of Cibber and Walpole in satire again is evident in *An Apology for the Life of Mrs. Shamela Andrews* by Conny Keyber.[11] Even the format of the title page mocks Cibber's book; and the dedication to "Miss Fanny" brings the Walpole cause under fire. "Miss Fanny" is Pope's name for John, Lord Hervey, Walpole's friend and propagandist, already satirized by Fielding as Miss Stitch in *Pasquin* (1736) and as John in *The Grub-Street Opera* (1731). In this latter play, an extended satire on Walpole and the royal family, we find the Parson Puzzletext whom we meet again in *Shamela,* superficially in the name of Tickletext, and in the very flesh as Williams.

---

[11] Fielding may have been helped to the full title of his satire by Richardson's preface to *Pamela: "further* Preface *or* Apology . . . [*is*] *unnecessary."*

Fielding's combined satirization of Cibber and Walpole—as with his rendering of the clergy—begins as early as *The Author's Farce* (1730). Cibber was the manager of Drury Lane Theater who would turn down young playwrights like Fielding. Cibber was called a plagiarist. Cibber was a standing joke about town as a Poet Laureate who could not write an ode. Cibber also stood for the Whig ministry of Sir Robert Walpole because his anti-Catholic and anti-Stuart play, *The Non-juror* (1717), had surely won him his laureateship. Young Fielding drew on this general fund—no doubt to settle a private account—when he comically set forth the playwright's troubles in *The Author's Farce,* but he (perhaps prudently) left politics alone except in once referring to Cibber as "Mr. Keyber." Fielding's audience in 1730 would not miss the point. Of the political reaction to *The Non-juror* Cibber himself writes in his *Apology:*

> . . . to none was I more beholden than to that celebrated author, Mr. Nathaniel Mist, whose *Weekly Journal,* for about fifteen years following, scarce ever fail'd of passing some of his party compliments upon me. The state and stage were his frequent parallels, and the ministers, and Minheer Keiber, the manager [Cibber was of Danish descent], were as constantly droll'd upon.

If by 1740 Mist's standing joke had begun to fade, Cibber's own book refreshed the memory. No one could miss the combined political and personal references when Fielding made Conny Keyber the author of *An Apology for the Life of Mrs. Shamela Andrews*—to expose the guile of

Pamela, "that young Politician." And "Conny," of course, looks like "Colley" and means rabbit or dupe. It has the further advantage of patting the head of Mr. Conyers Middleton.

When Conyers Middleton dedicated his *Life of Cicero* to Hervey, he unwittingly dedicated himself to Fielding's purpose. Middleton not only exalted one of Fielding's natural political enemies; he also in passing slighted the *Observations on the Life of Cicero* by Fielding's friend George Lyttelton. The *Life of Cicero* appeared in February, 1741, along with the second edition of *Pamela,* the edition—with new laudatory letters to the editor—which Parson Tickletext sends to Parson Oliver, the edition which seems to have set Fielding to work. Fielding neatly cut Middleton's dedication to fit "Miss Fanny." Turn to Fielding's opening sentence, for example, with Middleton's in mind:

> THE public will naturally expect, that in chusing a Patron for *the Life of* CICERO, I should address myself to some person of illustrious rank, distinguished by his parts and eloquence, and bearing a principal share in the great affairs of the Nation; who, according to the usual stile of Dedications, might be the proper subject of a comparison with the Hero of my piece.

Nothing in the dedication to Miss Fanny fails to use Middleton with utmost economy. Hervey is commended for following "the example of Your Noble Father" by making his own way into the House of Commons, and for "maintaining the rights of the people, yet asserting the prerogative of the Crown; measuring them both by the equal balance of the laws." Miss Fanny is commended for winning entrance to the ballroom by her charm and for balancing herself on the dance floor, though she perhaps leans too much to one (political) side. And Middleton's stylistic absurdities joined Cibber's under Fielding's attack. Where Conyers Middleton attributes his fine style to the periods of Cicero, Conny Keyber credits the rules of Euclid. We can appreciate the almost geometric nicety with which Middleton fitted Fielding's plan when we learn, as Brian Downs tells us, that Cibber himself was then considering his own subsequent study of Cicero.

In making Conny Keyber the author of *Shamela* Fielding implies (quite unjustly) that Cibber's *Apology* is scandalous. Of the author of *Shamela* John Puff writes—in parody of one of the letters introducing *Pamela:*

> Who is he, what is he that could write so excellent a Book? . . . he is able to draw every thing to Perfection but Virtue.

In *Joseph Andrews* Fielding, continuing to question Pamela's virtue, writes of Cibber's *Apology:*

> . . . this character of male-chastity . . . is almost the only virtue which the great Apologist hath not given himself for the sake of giving the example to his readers.

Cibber's "authorship" of *Shamela* simply serves Fielding's multidirectional satire. To suggest that Fielding actually thought Cibber wrote *Pamela*—a view stated by Dobson and repeated widely—seems to miss Fielding's complexity and perhaps to misread the text. Answering Tickletext's letter, Oliver intimates that the style which at first suggested Colley Cibber was soon conceded to be that of another.[12] "*Ciceronian* Eloquence" seems to refer rather to Middleton than to Cibber, as does:

I have seen a *Piece of his Performance,* where the Person, whose Life was written, could he have risen from the Dead again, would not have even suspected he had been aimed at, unless by the Title of the Book, which was superscribed with his Name.

Cicero might rise from the dead to confront the *Life* that had been aimed at him; Cibber outlived Fielding. When Fielding refers to "a Parson . . . *who writes Lives*" he surely means the Reverend Mr. Conyers Middleton, D.D.

But we must not be too literal. Fielding is satirizing bad writing in Cibber, Middleton, and the unknown author of *Pamela.* A man with Fielding's ear for language would not mistake one for either of the others. He had poked fun at Cibber's idiom in *The Champion.* He knew Middleton well enough to quote a long paragraph from the *Life of Cicero* in his *Enquiry into the Causes of the*

[12] Oliver's remark—"our Author's Professions of Modesty, which in my Youth I have heard at the Beginning of an Epilogue"—may indeed refer to the epilogue which Cibber wrote for Fielding's *Miser,* as Aurelien Digeon suggests (*The Novels of Fielding* [London, George Routledge & Sons, Ltd., 1925], p. 47, n. 1). But Oliver's remark hardly establishes that Fielding thought Cibber wrote *Pamela,* and it may refer only to the practice of covering up a bawdy play with a moral epilogue—spoken by an actress in tights.

Late Increase of Robbers (1751). The attention he gave Richardson's style may be easily ascertained by placing *Shamela* beside *Pamela*. He is merely enriching his burlesque of *Pamela* with references to two other books currently popular and currently damned. In *Joseph Andrews* (III, vi) he again pairs Middleton and Cibber as bad writers.

III

Fielding's criticism of Richardson is more basic, being close, indeed, to Fielding's criticism of life. To be sure, he ridicules the extravagant style of the letters prefatory to *Pamela,* and he mocks Richardson for telling his story in letters, particularly where Shamela records the action from her bed. But Fielding aims more especially at the vanity which led Richardson to prefix flattering letters, and at the hypocrisy in Richardson's pretending to be editor in order—it would seem—to praise his own book. In his first edition Richardson printed two letters flattering enough—Tickletext's "Little Book, charming *Pamela*" comes from the first of these—but to the second edition Richardson added twenty-four pages of letters, including a poem. In *Joseph Andrews* (I, i) Fielding continues to ridicule "the excellent essays or letters prefixed to the second and subsequent editions" of *Pamela*.[13] And in the

[13] Fielding apparently did not see the first edition, taking all the introductory letters to be new with the second (February 14, 1741). He therefore must have started *Shamela* sometime after the middle of February, and he must have finished it sometime before the middle of March to afford publication on April 4. Meanwhile the third edition of *Pamela* sailed past. Although

preface to *The Journal of a Voyage to Lisbon,* his last work, Fielding still seems to remember these letters, commenting on "the conduct of authors, who often fill a whole sheet with their own praises, to which they sometimes set their own real names, and sometimes a fictitious one." Within two more sentences he refers to Richardson himself. Fielding's satire, combined with friendly advice, perhaps caused Richardson to withdraw the introductory letters from the sixth edition (May 10, 1742), but they reappear in the seventh edition and (slightly abridged) in the eighth, Richardson's last.

First of the many attacks on *Pamela, Shamela* seems also to have had some effect on Richardson's continuation of *Pamela* (December, 1741). Delighted at catching the grave moralist at the keyhole, Fielding concentrates his forces against Richardson's two bedroom scenes. On his title page Richardson, somewhat defensively, had written that although his book "agreeably entertains" it is "intirely divested of all those Images, which, in too many Pieces calculated for Amusement only, tend to *inflame* the Minds they should *instruct.*" In Oliver's direct comment, in Tickletext's emotional responses, and in detailed travesty, Fielding answers Richardson's claim. And Richardson soon declares that in his sequel he intends "to avoid inflaming Descriptions"; and again, "that in the Two

---

Oliver thanks Tickletext for sending the second edition, Tickletext has suggested that Oliver and his neighboring clergymen must wait for the fourth edition to supply their pulpits. The composition of Tickletext's opening letter may thus postdate that of Oliver's reply.

new Volumes, I shall have no Occasion for such of the deep Scenes, as I believ'd necessary to the Story in two Places in the former." [14] Moreover, Richardson has Lady Davers defend at length Pamela's description of her "two grand Trials" as being indispensable to the story, adding ". . . it must be a very unvirtuous Mind, that can form any other Ideas from what you relate, than those of Terror and Pity for you."

But Fielding had formed ideas which bring Pamela's virtue seriously into question. He believed that Richardson pictured serving girls a good deal better than they should be: shortly before *Pamela* he commends Sir John Barnard's *Present for an Apprentice* for warning young men against female servants.[15] Moreover, behind Pamela's virtue Fielding seems again to have found the vanity and hypocrisy which for him were the essence of comedy. Pamela is unconsciously—sometimes coyly—vain in writing about the praises she receives, her humility, her Godliness, her clothes, and the overwhelming attentions of her young master. She is unconsciously a hypocrite as she strives to leave but wants to stay. Richardson wrote into his story the powerful attraction of the opulent Beast for his captive Beauty, who endures magic trials to be rewarded in the end—as Mr. B. turns into Prince Charming.[16] But Richardson, too intent with the object, could not see how it—or he—looked from a distance. Fielding

[14] McKillop, *op. cit.*, pp. 62-63.

[15] *Ibid.*, p. 35.

[16] Cf. Simon O. Lesser, "A Note on 'Pamela'," *College English*, XIV (1952), pp. 13-17.

simply turned into spirited calculation all of Pamela's unconscious bargaining. As he had done in *The Covent-Garden Tragedy,* Fielding had turned lofty seriousness concerning the passions of men and women into something like the business of the bawdy house.

That is the key to the satire in *Shamela,* but it does not open the way to all its brilliance. Once Pamela's virtue is turned upside down, the inversion of every other character and the manipulation of speech and action in rough mimicry of Richardson follow naturally enough. Indeed, we might expect Fielding, the experienced playwright, to take somewhat his own course. And actually we find Mrs. Jewkes more wholesome and the heroine more honest. But the real brilliance of *Shamela* comes from the precision of its parody, cut into a hundred facets. Phrase by phrase, taking advantage of every turn, Fielding harries Richardson to a finish. He had acquired the art in *Tom Thumb, The Covent-Garden Tragedy,* and *Tumble-Down Dick;* he had written brief parody in *The Champion;* he shared with his age the love of burlesque and satire. But nowhere before *Shamela* is his parody so sustained, so impertinent, and so close. Where Pamela sighs "O that I had never left my Rags and Poverty," Shamela remarks *"O! How I long to be in the Balconey at the Old House."* [17] Aaron Hill in his letter to the editor writes that the author

[17] The Drury Lane Playhouse, where Shamela's mother sold oranges. Others will perhaps take it to be a house of poorer repute. But the balcony at Drury Lane was sufficiently low for Fielding's purpose; and this theater, antedating Covent Garden by a century, was referred to as "the old house."

of *Pamela* "has stretch'd out this diminutive mere *Grain* of *Mustard-seed* (a poor Girl's little, innocent, Story) into a resemblance of . . . *Heaven.*" Fielding with the slightest of touches inserts his satirical thesis—Pamela is a harlot—and upsets into obscenity Hill's extravagance. He simply writes: "a poor Girl's little, &*c.*"

Even where Fielding seems to be extemporizing most freely in his own vein he is following Richardson. His mayor and aldermen might have walked in directly from his *Don Quixote in England* or *Pasquin* to engage Williams in wine and politics after dinner, robbing Shamela of his company. But the scene also imitates the arrival in *Pamela* of Mr. B.'s drinking companions on the eve of his wedding. And again, nothing is more germane to the Fielding countryside than Williams poaching Booby's hares with horse and hound. Yet as Williams rides off in the coach beside Booby's bride we realize that this is all a mime of the episode in *Pamela* where we find Williams walking, book in hand, at the meadowside, met, reconciled and finally taken into the coach by Pamela and Mr. B.:

Pray, Mr. *Williams,* oblige Pamela with your Hand; and step in yourself. He bow'd, and took my Hand, and my Master made him step in, and sit next me, all that ever he could do. . . .

Fielding reduces Richardson's two volumes to half a hundred pages, pinning scenes together with details from here and there (examine Shamela's relationship with Mrs. Jewkes), and yet following Richardson's contours exactly.

Few parodies—in verse or prose—can come near *Shamela* in its sustained and persistent mimicry.

The close parody of Richardson's bedroom scenes taught Fielding the high comedy of sex. To be sure, Fielding had for some time been writing comedies around the intrigues of the sexes. More than any of his contemporaries he emulates the Restoration playwrights. But his amorous scenes are heavy. The ladies of his plays know what they want, and they know themselves. We feel that young Fielding is so interested in sexual experience that he forgets its subtle connections with the rest of human nature. But *Shamela* is lit by an awareness of the comic incongruity of sex in civilized life. Pamela wants—not simply for prestige—to submit to her master, but everything she believes in prevents the desire from even breaking surface. In burlesquing this unconscious hypocrisy Fielding learned what it was. Fielding's stage ladies wish to appear proper only in the eyes of others; Lady Booby and Mrs. Slipslop wish to appear proper in their own eyes as well. A great deal of the comedy in Fielding's novels comes from the universal struggle of hidden passion against propriety, or, on the masculine side, of passion against the best of intentions. *Shamela,* more than anything before, brought this to the center of Fielding's comic vision.

Shamela draws together another significant element for Fielding the novelist. Fielding's habit of commenting upon his story can be seen already sketched into his plays: he repeatedly uses the convention of putting a supposed rehearsal on the stage, with author at one side commenting to the critics. In *Shamela* we find Parson Oliver commenting directly upon the immorality of *Pamela.* Oliver shows little of Fielding's later wit as intrusive narrator, but Oliver is similarly the wise head, assuring by plain statement that the satire does not backfire. Paralleling Richardson's own summary, Oliver enumerates the wayward lessons *Pamela* will be apt to teach. He upholds Fielding's aristocratic view that place should be kept. But more important, he declares one of Fielding's basic beliefs, the lesson he hoped to teach in *Tom Jones:* that prudence must not be overturned by passion. Oliver says that *Pamela* encourages young gentlemen to impetuous matches which will "sacrifice all the solid Comforts of their Lives, to a very transcient Satisfaction of a Passion. . . ." In *Tom Jones* Fielding seeks "to make good men wise" by instilling in them "that solid inward comfort of mind, which is the sure companion of innocence and virtue." Oliver writes of "the secure Satisfaction of a good Conscience, the Approbation of the Wise and Good, . . . and the extatick Pleasure of contemplating, that their Ways are acceptable to the Great Creator of the Universe." "But for Worldly Honours," Oliver continues, "they are often the Purchase of Force and Fraud. . . ." And Tom Jones cries out concerning Blifil who has defrauded him:

What is the poor pride arising from a magnificent house, a numerous equipage, a splendid table, and from all the other advantages or appearances of fortune compared to the warm, solid content, the swelling satisfaction, the thrilling transports, and the excellent triumphs which a good mind enjoys in the contemplation of a generous, virtuous, noble, benevolent action?

We may wish to concede that *Shamela* is coarse. We must certainly concede that it is hasty: when Shamela comes to Lincolnshire Fielding forgets that Mrs. Jewkes must have known all about her—the grapevine, we are told, is excellent—and Shamela had borne her child by Williams at the Lincolnshire estate. Mrs. Jervis and Mrs. Jewkes are confused in Fielding's mind: in the second edition he corrects an erroneous reference to Mrs. Jervis (present edition p. 16). Fielding seems to have read, digested and sharply parodied Richardson in a month's time, a month engaged also with political pamphleteering[18] and to some extent with a law practice and *The Champion*. But we cannot dismiss *Shamela* as trivial or ephemeral. Its place in the history of the novel is secure. Much of Fielding's mature comic genius is here. And it would be hard to find a better parody anywhere.

[18] *The Crisis: a Sermon* appeared in the same month with *Shamela;* both use the clergy for political satire.

TEXTUAL NOTE

The present edition transcribes the first edition (April 4, 1741; xv 59 pp.) from photostats of the Huntington Library copy corrected from a microfilm of the second edition (November 3, 1741; xv–56 pp.) in Yale University Library. The second edition seems to have been set up from the first edition, perhaps from a copy marked by Fielding. They are almost identical. A double line replaces a single line below Conny Keyber's name on the title page; the printer's ornament at the head of Tickletext's opening letter is changed. Pagination is identical through page 17. From page 18 forward, extra spaces between paragraphs are closed up, thus saving three pages. Page 19 starts the process of borrowing lines from the next page. Some errors are corrected; some remain; new ones occur. "Misreprsentations" on the title page stays misspelled, to be corrected only in Oliver Nelson's pirated Dublin edition (1741). Changes of such compounds as "your self" to "yourself" agree with Fielding's later usage. Alteration on the title page of "different from what" to "different from that which" and of *"Jervis"* to *"Jewkes"* in Oliver's first letter indicates an author's care. But irregularities in capitalization and punctuation suggest a helping hand, one attracted to lower-case letters. "Thing," "Time," and "no Doubt" are often made lower case, but

Fielding's later practice argues against accepting these changes as his. In general, all reasonable and consistent changes are taken to be Fielding's. (The title page of the first edition is here reproduced by permission of The Huntington Library, San Marino, California.) Several small errors in proof, untouched in the second edition, are also corrected.

AN APOLOGY FOR THE LIFE OF Mrs. SHAMELA ANDREWS.

In which, the many notorious FALSHOODS and MISREPRSENTATIONS of a Book called

PAMELA,

Are expoſed and refuted; and all the matchleſs ARTS of that young Politician, ſet in a true and juſt Light.

Together with

A full Account of all that paſſed between her and Parſon *Arthur Williams*; whoſe Character is repreſented in a manner ſomething different from what he bears in *PAMELA*. The whole being exact Copies of authentick Papers delivered to the Editor.

Neceſſary to be had in all FAMILIES.

By Mr. *CONNY KEYBER*.

LONDON:

Printed for A. DODD, at the *Peacock*, without *Temple-bar*.
M. DCC. XLI.

TO

MISS FANNY, &c.

MADAM,

IT *will be naturally expected, that when I write the Life of* Shamela, *I should dedicate it to some young Lady, whose Wit and Beauty might be the proper Subject of a Comparison with the Heroine of my Piece. This, those, who see I have done it in prefixing your Name to my Work, will much more confirmedly expect me to do; and, indeed, your Character would enable me to run some Length into a Parallel, tho' you, nor any one else, are at all like the matchless* Shamela.

You see, Madam, I have some Value for your Good-nature, when in a Dedication, which is properly a Panegyrick, I speak against, not for you; but I remember it is a Life which I am presenting you, and why should I expose my Veracity to any Hazard in the Front of the Work, considering what I have done in the Body. Indeed, I wish it was possible to write a Dedication, and get any thing by it, without one Word of Flattery; but since it is not, come on, and I hope to shew my Delicacy at least in the Compliments I intend to pay you.

First, *then, Madam, I must tell the World, that you have tickled up and brightened many Strokes in this Work by your Pencil.*

Secondly, *You have intimately conversed with me, one of the greatest Wits and Scholars of my Age.*

Thirdly, *You keep very good Hours, and frequently spend an useful Day before others begin to enjoy it. This I will take my Oath on; for I am admitted to your Presence in a Morning before other People's Servants are up; when I have constantly found you reading in good Books; and if ever I have drawn you upon me, I have always felt you very heavy.*

Fourthly, *You have a Virtue which enables you to rise early and study hard, and that is, forbearing to over-eat yourself, and this in spite of all the luscious Temptations of Puddings and Custards, exciting the Brute (as Dr.* Woodward *calls it) to rebel. This is a Virtue which I can greatly admire, though I much question whether I could imitate it.*

Fifthly, *A Circumstance greatly to your Honour, that by means of your extraordinary Merit and Beauty; you was carried into the Ball-Room at the* Bath, *by the discerning Mr.* Nash; *before the Age that other young Ladies generally arrived at that Honour, and while your Mamma herself existed in her perfect Bloom. Here you was observed in Dancing to balance your Body exactly, and to weigh every Motion with the exact and equal Measure of Time and Tune; and though you sometimes made a false Step, by leaning too much to one Side; yet every body said you would one Time or other, dance perfectly well, and uprightly.*

Sixthly, *I cannot forbear mentioning those pretty little Sonnets, and sprightly Compositions, which though they came from you with so much Ease, might be mentioned to the Praise of a great or grave Character.*

And now, Madam, I have done with you; it only remains to pay my Acknowledgments to an Author, whose Stile I have exactly followed in this Life, it being the properest for Biography. The Reader, I believe, easily guesses, I mean Euclid's Elements; *it was* Euclid *who taught me to write. It is you, Madam, who pay me for Writing. Therefore I am to both,*

A most Obedient, and

obliged humble Servant,

Conny Keyber.

LETTERS TO THE EDITOR.

THE EDITOR TO

HIMSELF.

Dear SIR,

HOWEVER you came by the excellent *Shamela,* out with it, without Fear or Favour, Dedication and all; believe me, it will go through many Editions, be translated into all Languages, read in all Nations and Ages, and to say a bold Word, it will do more good than the *C——y* have done harm in the World.

I am, Sir,

Sincerely your Well-wisher,

Yourself.

JOHN PUFF, *Esq; to the* EDITOR.

SIR,

I HAVE read your *Shamela* through and through, and a most inimitable Performance it is. Who is he, what is he that could write so excellent a Book? he must be doubtless most agreeable to the Age, and to *his Honour* himself; for he is able to draw every thing to Perfection but Virtue. Whoever the Author be, he hath one of the worst and most fashionable Hearts in the World, and I would recommend to him, in his next Performance, to undertake the Life of *his Honour*. For he who drew the Character of Parson *Williams,* is equal to the Task; nay he seems to have little more to do than to pull off the Parson's Gown, and *that* which makes him so agreeable to *Shamela,* and the Cap will fit.

I am, Sir,

Your humble Servant,

JOHN PUFF.

Note, Reader, several other COMMENDATORY LETTERS and COPIES of VERSES will be prepared against the NEXT EDITION.

AN

APOLOGY

for the life of

MRS. SHAMELA ANDREWS.

Parson Tickletext *to Parson* Oliver.

Rev. SIR,

HEREWITH I transmit you a Copy of sweet, dear, pretty *Pamela,* a little Book which this Winter hath produced; of which, I make no Doubt, you have already heard mention from some of your Neighbouring Clergy; for we have made it our common Business here, not only to cry it up, but to preach it up likewise: The Pulpit, as well as the Coffee-house, hath resounded with its Praise, and it is expected shortly, that his L——p will recommend it in a —— Letter to our whole Body.

And this Example, I am confident, will be imitated by all our Cloth in the Country: For besides speaking well of a Brother, in the Character of the Reverend Mr. *Williams,* the useful and truly religious Doctrine of *Grace* is every where inculcated.

This Book is the "Soul of *Religion,* Good-" Breeding, Discretion, Good-Nature, Wit, Fancy, " Fine Thought, and Morality. There is an Ease, " a natural Air, a dignified Simplicity, and measured Fullness in it, that resembling Life, " out-glows it. The Author hath reconciled the " *pleasing* to the *proper;* the Thought is every where " exactly cloathed by the Expression; and becomes " its Dress as *roundly* and as close as *Pamela* her " Country Habit; or *as she doth her no Habit,* " when modest Beauty seeks to hide itself, by cast-" ing off the Pride of Ornament, and displays itself " without any Covering;" which it frequently doth in this admirable Work, and presents Images to the Reader, which the coldest Zealot cannot read without Emotion.

For my own Part (and, I believe, I may say the same of all the Clergy of my Acquaintance) "I " have done nothing but read it to others, and hear " others again read it to me, ever since it came into " my Hands; and I find I am like to do nothing " else, for I know not how long yet to come: be-" cause if I lay the Book down *it comes after me.*

" When it has dwelt all Day long upon the Ear, it
" takes Possession all Night of the Fancy. It hath
" Witchcraft in every Page of it.——Oh! I feel an Emotion even while I am relating this: Methinks I see *Pamela* at this Instant, with all the Pride of Ornament cast off.

"Little Book, charming *Pamela*, get thee gone;
" face the World, in which thou wilt find nothing
" like thyself." Happy would it be for Mankind, if all other Books were burnt, that we might do nothing but read thee all Day, and dream of thee all Night. Thou alone art sufficient to teach us as much Morality as we want. Dost thou not teach us to pray, to sing Psalms, and to honour the Clergy? Are not these the whole Duty of Man? Forgive me, O Author of *Pamela,* mentioning the Name of a Book so unequal to thine: But, now I think of it, who is the Author, where is he, what is he, that hath hitherto been able to hide such an encircling, all-mastering Spirit, "he possesses every Quality that
" Art could have charm'd by: yet hath lent it to
" and concealed it in Nature. The Comprehensive-
" ness of his Imagination must be truly prodigious!
" It has stretched out this diminutive mere Grain
" of Mustard-seed (a poor Girl's little, *&c.*) into a
" Resemblance of that Heaven, which the best of
" good Books has compared it to."

To be short, this Book will live to the Age of the Patriarchs, and like them will carry on the good Work many hundreds of Years hence, among our Posterity, who will not HESITATE their Esteem with Restraint. If the *Romans* granted Exemptions to Men who begat a *few* Children for the Republick, what Distinction (if Policy and we should ever be reconciled) should we find to reward this Father of Millions, which are to owe Formation to the future Effect of his Influence.——I feel another Emotion.

As soon as you have read this yourself five or six Times over (which may possibly happen within a Week) I desire you would give it to my little God-Daughter, as a Present from me. This being the only Education we intend henceforth to give our Daughters. And pray let your Servant-Maids read it over, or read it to them. Both your self and the neighbouring Clergy, will supply yourselves for the Pulpit from the Booksellers, as soon as the fourth Edition is published. I am,

Sir,

Your most humble Servant,

THO. TICKLETEXT.

Parson Oliver *to Parson* Tickletext.

Rev. SIR,

I RECEIVED the Favour of yours with the inclosed Book, and really must own myself sorry, to see the Report I have heard of an epidemical Phrenzy now raging in Town, confirmed in the Person of my Friend.

If I had not known your Hand, I should, from the Sentiments and Stile of the Letter, have imagined it to have come from the Author of the famous Apology, which was sent me last Summer; and on my reading the remarkable Paragraph of *measured Fulness, that resembling Life out-glows it,* to a young Baronet, he cry'd out, *C——ly C——b—r* by G——. But I have since observed, that this, as well as many other Expressions in your Letter, was borrowed from those remarkable Epistles, which the Author, or the Editor hath prefix'd to the second Edition which you send me of his Book.

Is it possible that you or any of your Function can be in earnest, or think the Cause of Religion, or Morality, can want such slender Support? God forbid they should. As for Honour to the Clergy, I am sorry to see them so solicitous about it; for if worldly

Honour be meant, it is what their Predecessors in the pure and primitive Age, never had or sought. Indeed the secure Satisfaction of a good Conscience, the Approbation of the Wise and Good, (which never were or will be the Generality of Mankind) and the extatick Pleasure of contemplating, that their Ways are acceptable to the Great Creator of the Universe, will always attend those, who really deserve these Blessings: But for worldly Honours, they are often the Purchase of Force and Fraud, we sometimes see them in an eminent Degree possessed by Men, who are notorious for Luxury, Pride, Cruelty, Treachery, and the most abandoned Prostitution; Wretches who are ready to invent and maintain Schemes repugnant to the Interest, the Liberty, and the Happiness of Mankind, not to supply their Necessities, or even Conveniencies, but to pamper their Avarice and Ambition. And if this be the Road to worldly Honours, God forbid the Clergy should be even suspected of walking in it.

The History of *Pamela* I was acquainted with long before I received it from you, from my Neighbourhood to the Scene of Action. Indeed I was in hopes that young Woman would have contented herself with the Good-fortune she hath attained; and rather suffered her little Arts to have been forgotten than have revived their Remembrance, and endeavoured by perverting and misrepresenting Facts to be thought to deserve what she now enjoys: for though we do not imagine her the Author of the Narrative itself, yet we must suppose the Instructions were given by her, as well as the Reward, to the Composer. Who that is, though you so earnestly require of me, I shall leave you to guess from that *Ciceronian* Eloquence, with which the Work abounds; and that excellent Knack of making every Character amiable, which he lays his hands on.

But before I send you some Papers relating to this Matter, which will set *Pamela* and some others in a very different Light, than that in which they appear in the printed Book, I must beg leave to make some few Remarks on the Book itself, and its Tendency, (admitting it to be a true Relation,) towards improving Morality, or doing any good, either to the present Age, or Posterity: which when I have done, I shall, I flatter myself, stand excused from delivering it, either into the hands of my Daughter, or my Servant-Maid.

The Instruction which it conveys to Servant-Maids, is, I think, very plainly this, To look out for their Masters as sharp as they can. The Consequences of which will be, besides Neglect of their Business, and the using all manner of Means to come at Ornaments of their Persons, that if the Master is not a Fool, they will be debauched by him; and if he is a Fool, they will marry him. Neither of which, I apprehend, my good Friend, we desire should be the Case of our Sons.

And notwithstanding our Author's Professions of Modesty, which in my Youth I have heard at the Beginning of an Epilogue, I cannot agree that my Daughter should entertain herself with some of his Pictures; which I do not expect to be contemplated without Emotion, unless by one of my Age and Temper, who can see the Girl lie on her Back, with one Arm round Mrs. *Jewkes* and the other round the Squire, naked in Bed, with his Hand on her Breasts, *&c.* with as much Indifference as I read any other Page in the whole Novel. But surely this, and some other Descriptions, will not be put into the hands of his Daughter by any wise Man, though I believe it will be difficult for him to keep them from her; especially if the Clergy in Town have cried and preached it up as you say.

But, my Friend, the whole Narrative is such a Misrepresentation of Facts, such a Perversion of Truth, as you will, I am perswaded, agree, as soon as you have perused the Papers I now inclose to you, that I hope you or some other well-disposed Person, will communicate these Papers to the Publick, that this little Jade may not impose on the World, as she hath on her Master.

The true name of this Wench was SHAMELA, and not *Pamela,* as she stiles herself. Her Father had in his Youth the Misfortune to appear in no good Light at the *Old-Baily;* he afterwards served in the Capacity of a Drummer in one of the *Scotch* Regiments in the *Dutch* Service; where being drummed out, he came over to *England,* and turned Informer against several Persons on the late Gin-Act; and becoming acquainted with an Hostler at an Inn, where a *Scotch* Gentleman's Horses stood, he hath at last by his Interest obtain'd a pretty snug Place in the *Custom-house.* Her Mother sold Oranges in the Play-House; and whether she was married to her Father or no, I never could learn.

After this short Introduction, the rest of her History will appear in the following Letters, which I assure you are authentick.

LETTER I.

SHAMELA ANDREWS *to Mrs.* HENRIETTA MARIA HONORA ANDREWS *at her Lodgings at the* Fan *and* Pepper-Box *in* Drury-Lane.

Dear Mamma,

THIS comes to acquaint you, that I shall set out in the Waggon on *Monday,* desiring you to commodate me with a Ludgin, as near you as possible, in *Coulstin's-Court,* or *Wild-Street,* or somewhere thereabouts; pray let it be handsome, and not above two Stories high: For Parson *Williams* hath promised to visit me when he comes to Town, and I have got a good many fine Cloaths of the Old Put my Mistress's, who died a wil ago; and I beleve Mrs. *Jervis* will come along with me, for she says she would like to keep a House somewhere about *Short's-Gardens,* or towards *Queen-Street;* and if there was convenience for a *Bannio,* she should like it the better; but that she will settle herself when she comes to Town.——*O! How I long to be in the Balconey at the Old House*——so no more at present from

Your affectionate Daughter,

SHAMELA.

LETTER II.

Shamela Andrews *to* Henrietta Maria Honora Andrews.

Dear Mamma,

O what News, since I writ my last! the young Squire hath been here, and as sure as a Gun he hath taken a Fancy to me; *Pamela,* says he, (for so I am called here) you was a great Favourite of your late Mistress's; yes, an't please your Honour, says I; and I believe you deserved it, says he; thank your Honour for your good Opinion, says I; and then he took me by the Hand, and I pretended to be shy: Laud, says I, Sir, I hope you don't intend to be rude; no, says he, my Dear, and then he kissed me, 'till he took away my Breath——and I pretended to be Angry, and to get away, and then he kissed me again, and breathed very short, and looked very silly; and by Ill-Luck Mrs. *Jervis* came in, and had like to have spoiled Sport.—*How troublesome is such Interruption!* You shall hear now soon, for I shall not come away yet, so I rest,

Your affectionate Daughter,

SHAMELA.

LETTER III.

HENRIETTA MARIA HONORA ANDREWS
to SHAMELA ANDREWS.

Dear Sham,

YOUR last Letter hath put me into a great hurry of Spirits, for you have a very difficult Part to act. I hope you will remember your Slip with Parson *Williams,* and not be guilty of any more such Folly. Truly, a Girl who hath once known what is what, is in the highest Degree inexcusable if she respects her *Digressions;* but a Hint of this is sufficient. When Mrs. *Jervis* thinks of coming to Town, I believe I can procure her a good House, and fit for the Business; so I am,

Your affectionate Mother,

HENRIETTA MARIA HONORA ANDREWS.

LETTER IV

SHAMELA ANDREWS *to* HENRIETTA MARIA HONORA ANDREWS.

MARRY come up, good Madam, the Mother had never looked into the Oven for her Daughter, if she had not been there herself. I shall never have done if you upbraid me with having had a small One by *Arthur Williams,* when you yourself—but I say no more. *O! What fine Times when the Kettle calls the Pot.* Let me do what I will, I say my Prayers as often as another, and I read in good Books, as often as I have Leisure; and Parson *Williams* says, that will make amends.—So no more, but I rest

Your afflicted Daughter,

S——.

LETTER V.

HENRIETTA MARIA HONORA ANDREWS
to SHAMELA ANDREWS.

Dear Child,

WHY will you give such way to your Passion? How could you imagine I should be such a Simpleton, as to upbraid thee with being thy Mother's own Daughter! When I advised you not to be guilty of Folly, I meant no more than that you should take care to be well paid before-hand, and not trust to Promises, which a Man seldom keeps, after he hath had his wicked Will. And seeing you have a rich Fool to deal with, your not making a good Market will be the more inexcusable; indeed, with such Gentlemen as Parson *Williams,* there is more to be said; for they have nothing to give, and are commonly otherwise the best Sort of Men. I am glad to hear you read good Books, pray continue so to do. I have inclosed you one of Mr. *Whitefield's* Sermons, and also the Dealings with him, and am

Your affectionate Mother,

HENRIETTA MARIA, &c.

LETTER VI.

SHAMELA ANDREWS *to* HENRIETTA MARIA HONORA ANDREWS.

O MADAM, I have strange Things to tell you! As I was reading in that charming Book about the Dealings, in comes my Master—to be sure he is a precious One. *Pamela,* says he, what Book is that, I warrant you *Rochester's* Poems.—No, forsooth, says I, as pertly as I could; why how now Saucy Chops, Boldface, says he——Mighty pretty Words, says I, pert again.—Yes (says he) you are a d—d, impudent, stinking, cursed, confounded Jade, and I have a great Mind to kick your A——. You, kiss——says I. A-gad, says he, and so I will; with that he caught me in his Arms, and kissed me till he made my Face all over Fire. Now this served purely you know, to put upon the Fool for Anger. O! What precious Fools Men are! And so I flung from him in a mighty Rage, and pretended as how I would go out at the Door; but when I came to the End of the Room, I stood still, and my Master cryed out, Hussy, Slut, Saucebox, Boldface, come hither——Yes to be sure, says I; why don't you come, says he; what should I come for, says I; if you don't come to me, I'll come to you, says he; I shan't come to you I assure you, says I. Upon which he run up, caught me in his Arms, and flung me upon a Chair, and began to offer to touch my Under-Petticoat. Sir, says I, you had better not offer to be rude; well, says he, no more I won't then; and away he went out of the Room. I was so mad to be sure I could have cry'd.

Oh what a prodigious Vexation it is to a Woman to be made a Fool of.

Mrs. *Jervis,* who had been without, harkening, now came to me. She burst into a violent Laugh the Moment she came in. Well, says she, as soon as she could speak, I have Reason to bless myself that I am an Old Woman. Ah Child! if you had known the Jolly Blades of my Age, you would not have been left in the Lurch in this manner. Dear Mrs. *Jervis,* says I, don't laugh at one; and to be sure I was a little angry with her.——Come, says she, my dear Honeysuckle, I have one Game to play for you; he shall see you in Bed; he shall, my little Rosebud, he shall see those pretty, little, white, round, panting ——and offer'd to pull off my Handkerchief.—Fie, Mrs. *Jervis,* says I, you make me blush, and upon my Fackins, I believe she did: She went on thus. I know the Squire likes you, and notwithstanding the Aukwardness of his Proceeding, I am convinced hath some hot Blood in his Veins, which will not let him rest, 'till he hath communicated some of his Warmth to thee my little Angel; I heard him last Night at our Door, trying if it was open, now to-night I will take care it shall be so; I warrant that he makes the second Trial; which if he doth, he shall find us ready to receive him. I will at first counterfeit Sleep, and after a Swoon; so that he will have you naked in his Possession: and then if you are disappointed, a Plague of all young Squires, say I.—— And so, Mrs. *Jervis,* says I, you would have me yield myself to him, would you; you would have me be a second Time a Fool for nothing. Thank you for that, Mrs. *Jervis*. For nothing! marry forbid, says she, you know he hath large Sums of Money, besides abundance of fine Things; and do you think, when you have inflamed him, by giving his Hand a Liberty, with that charming Person; and that you know he may easily think he obtains against your Will, he will not give any thing to come at all——. This will not do, Mrs. *Jervis,* answered I. I have heard my Mamma say, (and so you know, Madam, I have) that in her Youth, Fellows have often taken away in the Morning, what they gave over Night. No, Mrs. *Jervis,* nothing under a regular taking into Keeping, a settled Settlement, for me, and all my Heirs, all my whole Lifetime, shall do the Business——or else crosslegged, is the Word, faith, with *Sham;* and then I snapt my Fingers.

Thursday Night, Twelve o'Clock.

Mrs. *Jervis* and I are just in Bed, and the Door unlocked; if my Master should come—Odsbobs! I hear him just coming in at the Door. You see I write in the present Tense, as Parson *Williams* says. Well, he is in Bed between us, we both shamming a Sleep, he steals his Hand into my Bosom, which I, as if in my Sleep, press close to me with mine, and then pretend to awake.—I no sooner see him, but I scream out to Mrs. *Jervis,* she feigns likewise but just to come to herself; we both begin, she to becall, and I to bescratch very liberally. After having made a pretty free Use of my Fingers, without any great Regard to the Parts I attack'd, I counterfeit a Swoon. Mrs. *Jervis* then cries out, O, Sir, what have you done, you have murthered poor *Pamela:* she is gone, she is gone.——

O what a Difficulty it is to keep one's Countenance, when a violent Laugh desires to burst forth.

The poor Booby frightned out of his Wits, jumped out of Bed, and, in his Shirt, sat down by my Bed-Side, pale and trembling, for the Moon shone, and I kept my Eyes wide open, and pretended to fix them in my Head. Mrs. *Jervis* apply'd Lavender

Water, and Hartshorn, and this, for a full half Hour; when thinking I had carried it on long enough, and being likewise unable to continue the Sport any longer, I began by Degrees to come to my self.

The Squire who had sat all this while speechless, and was almost really in that Condition, which I feigned, the Moment he saw me give Symptoms of recovering my Senses, fell down on his Knees; and O *Pamela,* cryed he, can you forgive me, my injured Maid? by Heaven, I know not whether you are a Man or a Woman, unless by your swelling Breasts. Will you promise to forgive me: I forgive you! D—n you (says I) and d—n you says he, if you come to that. I wish I had never seen your bold Face, saucy Sow, and so went out of the Room.

O what a silly Fellow is a bashful young Lover!

He was no sooner out of hearing, as we thought, than we both burst into a violent Laugh. Well, says Mrs. *Jervis,* I never saw any thing better acted than your Part: But I wish you may not have discouraged him from any future Attempt; especially since his Passions are so cool, that you could prevent his Hands going further than your Bosom. Hang him, answer'd I, he is not quite so cold as that I assure you; our Hands, on neither Side, were idle in the

Scuffle, nor have left us any Doubt of each other as to that matter.

Friday Morning.

My Master sent for Mrs. *Jervis,* as soon as he was up, and bid her give an Account of the Plate and Linnen in her Care; and told her, he was resolved that both she and the little Gipsy (I'll assure him) should set out together. Mrs. *Jervis* made him a saucy Answer; which any Servant of Spirit, you know, would, tho' it should be one's Ruin; and came immediately in Tears to me, crying, she had lost her Place on my Account, and that she should be forced to take to a House, as I mentioned before; and that she hoped I would, at least, make her all the amends in my power, for her Loss on my Account, and come to her House whenever I was sent for. Never fear, says I, I'll warrant we are not so near being turned away, as you imagine; and, i'cod, now it comes into my Head, I have a Fetch for him, and you shall assist me in it. But it being now late, and my Letter pretty long, no more at present from

Your Dutiful Daughter,

SHAMELA.

LETTER VII.

Mrs. Lucretia Jervis *to* Henrietta Maria Honora Andrews.

Madam,

Miss *Sham* being set out in a Hurry for my Master's House in *Lincolnshire,* desired me to acquaint you with the Success of her Stratagem, which was to dress herself in the plain Neatness of a Farmer's Daughter, for she before wore the Cloaths of my late Mistress, and to be introduced by me as a Stranger to her Master. To say the Truth, she became the Dress extremely, and if I was to keep a House a thousand Years, I would never desire a prettier Wench in it.

As soon as my Master saw her, he immediately threw his Arms round her Neck, and smothered her with Kisses (for indeed he hath but very little to say for himself to a Woman.) He swore that *Pamela* was an ugly Slut (pardon, dear Madam, the Courseness of the Expression) compared to such divine Excellence. He added, he would turn *Pamela* away immediately, and take this new Girl, whom he

thought to be one of his Tenant's Daughters in her room.

Miss *Sham* smiled at these Words, and so did your humble Servant, which he perceiving looked very earnestly at your fair Daughter, and discovered the Cheat.

How, *Pamela,* says he, is it you? I thought, Sir, said Miss, after what had happened, you would have known me in any Dress. No, Hussy, says he, but after what hath happened, I should know thee out of any Dress from all thy Sex. He then was what we Women call rude, when done in the Presence of others; but it seems it is not the first time, and Miss defended herself with great Strength and Spirit.

The Squire, who thinks her a pure Virgin, and who knows nothing of my Character, resolved to send her into *Lincolnshire,* on Pretence of conveying her home; where our old Friend *Nanny Jewkes* is Housekeeper, and where Miss had her small one by Parson *Williams* about a Year ago. This is a Piece of News communicated to us by *Robin* Coachman, who is intrusted by his Master to carry on this Affair privately for him: But we hang together, I believe, as well as any Family of Servants in the Nation.

You will, I believe, Madam, wonder that the

Squire, who doth not want Generosity, should never have mentioned a Settlement all this while, I believe it slips his Memory: But it will not be long first, no Doubt: For, as I am convinced the young Lady will do nothing unbecoming your Daughter, nor ever admit him to taste her Charms, without something sure and handsome before-hand; so, I am certain, the Squire will never rest till they have danced *Adam* and *Eve*'s kissing Dance together. Your Daughter set out yesterday Morning, and told me, as soon as she arrived, you might depend on hearing from her.

Be pleased to make my Compliments acceptable to Mrs. *Davis* and Mrs. *Silvester,* and Mrs. *Jolly,* and all Friends, and permit me the Honour, Madam, to be with the utmost Sincerity,

Your most Obedient

Humble Servant

LUCRETIA JERVIS.

If the Squire should continue his Displeasure against me, so as to insist on the Warning he hath given me, you will see me soon, and I will lodge in the same House with you, if you have room, till I can provide for my self to my Liking.

MOTHER

LETTER VIII.

HENRIETTA MARIA HONORA ANDREWS
to LUCRETIA JERVIS.

Madam,

I RECEIVED the Favour of your Letter, and I find you have not forgot your usual Poluteness, which you learned when you was in keeping with a Lord.

I am very much obliged to you for your Care of my Daughter, am glad to hear she hath taken such good Resolutions, and hope she will have sufficient Grace to maintain them.

All Friends are well and remember to you. You will excuse the Shortness of this Scroll; for I have sprained my right Hand, with boxing three new made Officers.—Tho' to my Comfort, I beat them all. I rest,

Your Friend and Servant,

HENRIETTA, &c.

LETTER IX.

SHAMELA ANDREWS *to* HENRIETTA MARIA HONORA ANDREWS.

Dear Mamma,

I SUPPOSE Mrs. *Jervis* acquainted you with what past 'till I left *Bedfordshire;* whence I am after a very pleasant Journey arrived in *Lincolnshire,* with your old Acquaintance Mrs. *Jewkes,* who formerly helped Parson *Williams* to me; and now designs I see, to sell me to my Master; thank her for that; she will find two Words go to that Bargain.

The Day after my Arrival here, I received a Letter from Mr. *Williams,* and as you have often desired to see one from him, I have inclosed it to you; it is, I think, the finest I ever received from that charming Man, and full of a great deal of Learning.

O! What a brave Thing it is to be a Scholard, and to be able to talk Latin.

Parson WILLIAMS *to* PAMELA ANDREWS.

Mrs. Pamela,

HAVING learnt by means of my Clerk, who Yesternight visited the Rev[d]. Mr. *Peters* with my Commands, that you are returned into this County, I purposed to have saluted your fair Hands this Day towards Even: But am obliged to sojourn this Night at a neighbouring Clergyman's; where we are to pierce a Virgin Barrel of Ale, in a Cup of which I shall not be unmindful to celebrate your Health.

I hope you have remembered your Promise, to bring me a leaden Canister of Tobacco (the Saffron Cut) for in Troth, this Country at present affords nothing worthy the replenishing a Tube with.—— Some I tasted the other Day at an Alehouse, gave me the Heart-Burn, tho' I filled no oftner than five Times.

I was greatly concerned to learn, that your late Lady left you nothing, tho' I cannot say the Tidings much surprized me: For I am too intimately acquainted with the Family; (myself, Father and Grandfather having been successive Incumbents on the same Cure, which you know is in their Gift) I say, I am too well acquainted with them to expect much from their Generosity. They are in Verity, as worthless a Family as any other whatever. The young Gentleman I am informed, is a perfect Reprobate; that he hath an *Ingenium Versatile* to every Species of Vice, which, indeed, no one can much wonder at, who animadverts on that want of Respect to the Clergy, which was observable in him when a Child. I remember when he was at the Age of Eleven only, he met my Father without either pulling off his Hat, or riding out of the way. Indeed, a Contempt of the Clergy is the fashionable Vice of the Times; but let such Wretches know, they cannot hate, detest, and despise us, half so much as we do them.

However, I have prevailed on myself to write a civil Letter to your Master, as there is a Probability of his being shortly in a Capacity of rendring me a Piece of Service; my good Friend and Neighbour the Rev[d]. Mr. *Squeeze-Tithe* being, as I am informed by one whom I have employed to attend for that Purpose, very near his Dissolution.

You see, sweet Mrs. *Pamela,* the Confidence with which I dictate these Things to you; whom after those Endearments which have passed between us, I must in some Respects estimate as my Wife: For tho' the Omission of the Service was a Sin; yet, as I have told you, it was a venial One, of which I have truly repented, as I hope you have; and also that you have continued the wholesome Office of reading good Books, and are improved in your Psalmody, of which I shall have a speedy Trial: For I purpose to give you a Sermon next *Sunday*, and shall spend the Evening with you, in Pleasures, which tho' not strictly innocent, are however to be purged away by frequent and sincere Repentance. I am,

Sweet Mrs. Pamela,

Your faithful Servant,

ARTHUR WILLIAMS.

You find, Mamma, what a charming way he hath of Writing, and yet I assure you, that is not the most charming Thing belonging to him: For, tho' he doth not put any Dears, and Sweets, and Loves into his Letters, yet he says a thousand of them: For he can be as fond of a Woman, as any Man living.

Sure Women are great Fools, when they prefer a laced Coat to the Clergy, whom it is our Duty to honour and respect.

Well, on *Sunday* Parson *Williams* came, according to his Promise, and an excellent Sermon he preached; his Text was, *Be not Righteous overmuch;* and, indeed, he handled it in a very fine way; he shewed us that the Bible doth not require too much Goodness of us, and that People very often call things Goodness that are not so. That to go to Church, and to pray, and to sing Psalms, and to honour the Clergy, and to repent, is true Religion; and 'tis not doing good to one another, for that is one of the greatest Sins we can commit, when we don't do it for the sake of Religion. That those People who talk of Vartue and Morality, are the wickedest of all Persons. That 'tis not what we do, but what we believe, that must save us, and a great many other good Things; I wish I could remember them all.

As soon as Church was over, he came to the Squire's House, and drank Tea with Mrs. *Jewkes* and me; after which Mrs. *Jewkes* went out and left us together for an Hour and half——Oh! he is a charming Man.

After Supper he went Home, and then Mrs. *Jewkes* began to catechize me, about my Familiarity with him. I see she wants him herself. Then she proceeded to tell me what an Honour my Master did me in liking me, and that it was both an inexcusable

Folly and Pride in me, to pretend to refuse him any Favour. Pray, Madam, says I, consider I am a poor Girl, and have nothing but my Modesty to trust to. If I part with that, what will become of me. Methinks, says she, you are not so mighty modest when you are with Parson *Williams;* I have observed you gloat at one another, in a Manner that hath made me blush. I assure you, I shall let the Squire know what sort of Man he is; you may do your Will, says I, as long as he hath a Vote for Pallamant-Men, the Squire dares do nothing to offend him; and you will only shew that you are jealous of him, and that's all. How now, Mynx, says she; Mynx! No more Mynx than yourself, says I; with that she hit me a Slap on the Shoulder, and I flew at her and scratched her Face, i'cod, 'till she went crying out of the Room; so no more at Present, from

Your Dutiful Daughter,

SHAMELA.

LETTER X.

SHAMELA ANDREWS *to* HENRIETTA MARIA HONORA ANDREWS.

O MAMMA! Rare News! As soon as I was up this Morning, a Letter was brought me from the Squire, of which I send you a Copy.

Squire BOOBY *to* PAMELA.

Dear Creature,

I HOPE you are not angry with me for the Deceit put upon you, in conveying you to *Lincolnshire,* when you imagined yourself going to *London.* Indeed, my dear *Pamela,* I cannot live without you; and will very shortly come down and convince you, that my Designs are better than you imagine, and such as you may with Honour comply with. I am,

My Dear Creature,

Your doating Lover,

BOOBY.

Now, Mamma, what think you?—For my own Part, I am convinced he will marry me, and faith so he shall. O! Bless me! I shall be Mrs. *Booby,* and be Mistress of a great Estate, and have a dozen Coaches and Six, and a fine House at *London,* and another at *Bath,* and Servants, and Jewels, and Plate, and go to Plays, and Opera's, and Court; and do what I will, and spend what I will. But, poor Parson *Williams!* Well; and can't I see Parson *Williams,* as well after Marriage as before: For I shall never care a Farthing for my Husband. No, I hate and despise him of all Things.

Well, as soon as I had read my Letter, in came Mrs. *Jewkes.* You see, Madam, says she, I carry the Marks of your Passion about me; but I have received Order from my Master to be civil to you, and I must obey him: For he is the best Man in the World, notwithstanding your Treatment of him. My Treatment of him; Madam, says I? Yes, says she, your Insensibility to the Honour he intends you, of making you his Mistress. I would have you to know, Madam, I would not be Mistress to the greatest King, no nor Lord in the Universe. I value my Vartue more than I do any thing my Master can give me; and so we talked a full Hour and a half, about my Vartue; and I was afraid at first, she had heard something about the Bantling, but I find

she hath not; tho' she is as jealous, and suspicious, as old Scratch.

In the Afternoon, I stole into the Garden to meet Mr. *Williams;* I found him at the Place of his Appointment, and we staid in a kind of Arbour, till it was quite dark. He was very angry when I told him what Mrs. *Jewkes* had threatned——Let him refuse me the Living, says he, if he dares, I will vote for the other Party; and not only so, but will expose him all over the Country. I owe him 150*l.* indeed, but I don't care for that; by that Time the Election is past, I shall be able to plead the *Statue* of *Lamentations.*

I could have stayed with the dear Man for ever, but when it grew dark, he told me, he was to meet the neighbouring Clergy, to finish the Barrel of Ale they had tapped the other Day, and believed they should not part till three or four in the Morning——So he left me, and I promised to be penitent, and go on with my reading in good Books.

As soon as he was gone, I bethought myself, what Excuse I should make to Mrs. *Jewkes,* and it came into my Head to pretend as how I intended to drown myself; so I stript off one of my Petticoats, and threw it into the Canal; and then I went and hid myself in the Coal-hole, where I lay all Night; and comforted myself with repeating over some Psalms, and other good things, which I had got by heart.

In the Morning Mrs. *Jewkes* and all the Servants were frighted out of their Wits, thinking I had run away; and not devising how they should answer it to their Master. They searched all the likeliest Places they could think of for me, and at last saw my Petticoat floating in the Pond. Then they got a Drag-Net, imagining I was drowned, and intending to drag me out; but at last *Moll* Cook coming for some Coals, discovered me lying all along in no very good Pickle. Bless me! Mrs. *Pamela,* says she, what can be the Meaning of this? I don't know, says I, help me up, and I will go in to Breakfast, for indeed I am very hungry. Mrs. *Jewkes* came in immediately, and was so rejoyced to find me alive, that she asked with great Good-Humour, where I had been? and how my Petticoat came into the Pond. I answered, I believed the Devil had put it into my Head to drown my self; but it was a Fib; for I never saw the Devil in my Life, nor I don't believe he hath any thing to do with me.

So much for this Matter. As soon as I had breakfasted, a Coach and Six came to the Door, and who should be in it but my Master.

I immediately run up into my Room, and stript, and washed, and drest my self as well as I could, and put on my prettiest round-ear'd Cap, and pulled down my Stays, to shew as much as I could of my Bosom, (for Parson *Williams* says, that is the most beautiful part of a Woman) and then I practised over all my Airs before the Glass, and then I sat down and read a Chapter in the Whole Duty of Man.

Then Mrs. *Jewkes* came to me and told me, my Master wanted me below, and says she, Don't behave like a Fool; No, thinks I to my self, I believe I shall find Wit enough for my Master and you too.

So down goes I into the Parlour to him. *Pamela,* says he, the Moment I came in, you see I cannot stay long from you, which I think is a sufficient Proof of the Violence of my Passion. Yes, Sir, says I, I see your Honour intends to ruin me, that nothing but the Destruction of my Vartue will content you.

O what a charming Word that is, rest his Soul who first invented it.

How can you say I would ruin you, answered the Squire, when you shall not ask any thing which I will not grant you. If that be true, says I, good your Honour let me go Home to my poor but honest Parents; that is all I have to ask, and do not ruin a poor Maiden, who is resolved to carry her Vartue to the Grave with her.

Hussy, says he, don't provoke me, don't provoke

me, I say. You are absolutely in my power, and if you won't let me lie with you by fair Means, I will by Force. O La, Sir, says I, I don't understand your paw Words.—Very pretty Treatment indeed, says he, to say I use paw Words; Hussy, Gipsie, Hypocrite, Saucebox, Boldface, get out of my Sight, or I will lend you such a Kick in the—I don't care to repeat the Word, but he meant my hinder part. I was offering to go away, for I was half afraid, when he called me back, and took me round the Neck and kissed me, and then bid me go about my Business.

I went directly into my Room, where Mrs. *Jewkes* came to me soon afterwards. So Madam, says she, you have left my Master below in a fine Pet, he hath threshed two or three of his Men already: It is mighty pretty that all his Servants are to be punished for your Impertinence.

Harkee, Madam, says I, don't you affront me, for if you do, d—n me (I am sure I have repented for using such a Word) if I am not revenged.

How sweet is Revenge: Sure the Sermon Book is in the Right, in calling it the sweetest Morsel the Devil ever dropped into the Mouth of a Sinner.

Mrs. *Jewkes* remembered the Smart of my Nails too well to go farther, and so we sat down and talked about my Vartue till Dinner-time, and then I was sent for to wait on my Master. I took care to be often caught looking at him, and then I always turn'd away my Eyes, and pretended to be ashamed. As soon as the Cloth was removed, he put a Bumper of Champagne into my Hand, and bid me drink ——O la I can't name the Health. Parson *Williams* may well say he is a wicked Man.

Mrs. *Jewkes* took a Glass and drank the dear *Monysyllable;* I don't understand that Word, but I believe it is baudy. I then drank towards his Honour's good Pleasure. Ay, Hussy, says he, you can give me Pleasure if you will; Sir, says I, I shall be always glad to do what is in my power, and so I pretended not to know what he meant. Then he took me into his Lap.—O Mamma, I could tell you something if I would—and he kissed me—and I said I won't be slobber'd about so, so I won't; and he bid me get out of the Room for a saucy Baggage, and said he had a good mind to spit in my Face.

Sure no Man ever took such a Method to gain a Woman's Heart.

I had not been long in my Chamber before Mrs. *Jewkes* came to me, and told me, my Master would not see me any more that Evening, that is, if he can help it; for, added she, I easily perceive the great Ascendant you have over him; and to confess the Truth, I don't doubt but you will shortly be my Mistress.

What says I, dear Mrs. *Jewkes,* what do you say? Don't flatter a poor Girl, it is impossible his Honour can have any honourable Design upon me. And so we talked of honourable Designs till Supper-time. And Mrs. *Jewkes* and I supped together upon a hot buttered Apple-Pie; and about ten o' Clock we went to Bed.

We had not been a Bed half an Hour, when my Master came pit a pat into the Room in his Shirt as before, I pretended not to hear him, and Mrs. *Jewkes* laid hold of one Arm, and he pulled down the Bed-cloaths and came into Bed on the other Side, and took my other Arm and laid it under him, and fell a kissing one of my Breasts as if he would have devoured it; I was then forced to awake, and began to struggle with him, Mrs. *Jewkes* crying why don't you do it? I have one Arm secure, if you can't deal with the rest I am sorry for you. He was as rude as possible to me; but I remembered, Mamma, the Instructions you gave me to avoid being ravished, and followed them, which soon brought him to Terms, and he promised me on quitting my hold, that he would leave the Bed.

O Parson Williams, *how little are all the Men in the World compared to thee.*

My Master was as good as his Word; upon which Mrs. *Jewkes* said, O Sir, I see you know very little of our *Sect,* by parting so easily from the Blessing when you was so near it. No, Mrs. *Jewkes,* answered he, I am very glad no more hath happened, I would not have injured *Pamela* for the World. And to-morrow Morning perhaps she may hear of something to her Advantage. This she may be certain of, that I will never take her by Force, and then he left the Room.

What think you now, Mrs. *Pamela,* says Mrs. *Jewkes,* Are you not yet persuaded my Master hath honourable Designs? I think he hath given no great Proof of them to-night, said I. Your Experience I find is not great, says she, but I am convinced you will shortly be my Mistress, and then what will become of poor me.

With such Sort of Discourse we both fell asleep. Next Morning early my Master sent for me, and after kissing me, gave a Paper into my Hand which he bid me read; I did so, and found it to be a Proposal for settling 250*l*. a Year on me, besides several other advantagious Offers, as Presents of Money and other Things. Well, *Pamela,* said he, what Answer do you make me to this. Sir, said I, I value my Vartue more than all the World, and I had rather be the poorest Man's Wife, than the richest Man's Whore. You are a Simpleton, said he; That may be, and yet I may have as much Wit as some Folks, cry'd I; meaning me, I suppose, said he; every Man knows himself best, says I. Hussy, says he, get out of the Room, and let me see your saucy Face no more, for I find I am in more Danger than you are, and therefore it shall be my Business to avoid you as much as I can; and it shall be mine, thinks I, at every turn to throw my self in your Way. So I went out, and as I parted, I heard him sigh and say he was bewitched.

Mrs. *Jewkes* hath been with me since, and she assures me she is convinced I shall shortly be Mistress of the Family, and she really behaves to me, as if she already thought me so. I am resolved now to aim at it. I thought once of making a little Fortune by my Person. I now intend to make a great one by my Vartue. So asking Pardon for this long Scroll, I am,

Your dutiful Daughter,

SHAMELA.

LETTER XI.

Henrietta Maria Honora Andrews *to* Shamela Andrews.

Dear Sham,

I received your last Letter with infinite Pleasure, and am convinced it will be your own Fault if you are not married to your Master, and I would advise you now to take no less Terms. But, my dear Child, I am afraid of one Rock only, That Parson *Williams,* I wish he was out of the Way. A Woman never commits Folly but with such Sort of Men, as by many Hints in the Letters I collect him to be: but, consider, my dear Child, you will hereafter have Opportunities sufficient to indulge yourself with Parson *Williams,* or any other you like. My Advice therefore to you is, that you would avoid seeing him any more till the Knot is tied. Remember the first Lesson I taught you, that a married Woman injures only her Husband, but a single Woman herself. I am, in hopes of seeing you a great Lady,

Your affectionate Mother,

HENRIETTA MARIA, &c.

The following Letter seems to have been written before *Shamela* received the last from her Mother.

LETTER XII.

SHAMELA ANDREWS *to* HENRIETTA MARIA HONORA ANDREWS.

Dear Mamma,

I LITTLE feared when I sent away my last, that all my Hopes would be so soon frustrated; but I am certain you will blame Fortune and not me. To proceed then. About two Hours after I had left the Squire, he sent for me into the Parlour. *Pamela,* said he, and takes me gently by the Hand, will you walk with me in the Garden; yes, Sir, says I, and pretended to tremble; but I hope your Honour will not be rude. Indeed, says he, you have nothing to fear from me, and I have something to tell you, which if it doth not please you, cannot offend. We walked out together, and he began thus, *Pamela,* will you tell me Truth? Doth the Resistance you make to my Attempts proceed from Vartue only, or have I not some Rival in thy dear Bosom who might be more successful? Sir, says I, I do assure you I never had a thought of any Man in the World. How says he, not of Parson *Williams!* Parson *Williams,* says I, is the last Man upon Earth; and if I was a Dutchess, and your Honour was to make your Addresses to me, you would have no Reason to be jealous of any Rival, especially such a Fellow as Parson *Williams.* If ever I had a Liking, I am sure —but I am not worthy of you one Way, and no Riches should ever bribe me the other. My Dear, says he, you are worthy of every Thing, and suppose I should lay aside all Considerations of Fortune, and disregard the Censure of the World, and marry you. O Sir, says I, I am sure you can have no such Thoughts, you cannot demean your self so low. Upon my Soul, I am in earnest, says he,——O Pardon me, Sir, says I, you can't persuade me of this. How Mistress, says he, in a violent Rage, do you give me the Lie? Hussy, I have a great mind to box your saucy Ears, but I am resolved I will never put it in your power to affront me again, and therefore I desire you to prepare your self for your Journey this Instant. You deserve no better Vehicle than a Cart; however, for once you shall have a Chariot, and it shall be ready for you within this half Hour; and so he flung from me in a Fury.

What a foolish Thing it is for a Woman to dally too long with her Lover's Desires; how many have owed their being old Maids to their holding out too long.

Mrs. *Jewkes* came to me presently, and told me, I must make ready with all the Expedition imaginable, for that my Master had ordered the Chariot, and that if I was not prepared to go in it, I should be turned out of Doors, and left to find my way Home on Foot. This startled me a little, yet I resolved, whether in the right or wrong, not to submit nor ask Pardon: For that you know, Mamma, you never could your self bring me to from my Childhood: Besides, I thought he would be no more able to master his Passion for me now, than he had been hitherto; and if he sent two Horses away with me, I concluded he would send four to fetch me back. So, truly, I resolved to brazen it out, and with all the Spirit I could muster up, I told Mrs. *Jewkes* I was vastly pleased with the News she brought me; that no one ever went more readily than I should, from a Place where my Vartue had been in continual Danger. That as for my Master, he might easily get those who were fit for his Purpose; but, for my Part, I preferred my Vartue to all Rakes whatever ——And for his Promises, and his Offers to me,

I don't value them of a Fig—Not of a Fig, Mrs. *Jewkes;* and then I snapt my Fingers.

Mrs. *Jewkes* went in with me, and helped me to pack up my little All, which was soon done; being no more than two Day-Caps, two Night-Caps, five Shifts, one Sham, a Hoop, a Quilted-Petticoat, two Flannel-Petticoats, two pair of Stockings, one odd one, a pair of lac'd Shoes, a short flowered Apron, a lac'd Neck-Handkerchief, one Clog, and almost another, and some few Books: as, *A full Answer to a plain and true Account,* &c. *The Whole Duty of Man,* with only the Duty to one's Neighbour, torn out. Thc Third Volume of the *Atalantis. Venus in the Cloyster: Or, the Nun in her Smock. God's Dealings with Mr. Whitefield. Orfus and Eurydice.* Some Sermon-Books; and two or three Plays, with their Titles, and Part of the first Act torn off.

So as soon as we had put all this into a Bundle, the Chariot was ready, and I took leave of all the Servants, and particularly Mrs. *Jewkes,* who pretended, I believe, to be more sorry to part with me than she was; and then crying out with an Air of Indifference, my Service to my Master, when he condescends to enquire after me, I flung my self into the Chariot, and bid *Robin* drive on.

We had not gone far, before a Man on Horseback, riding full Speed, overtook us, and coming up to the Side of the Chariot, threw a Letter into the Window, and then departed without uttering a single Syllable.

I immediately knew the Hand of my dear *Williams,* and was somewhat surprized, tho' I did not apprehend the Contents to be so terrible, as by the following exact Copy you will find them.

Parson WILLIAMS *to* PAMELA.

Dear Mrs. Pamela,

THAT Disrespect for the Clergy, which I have formerly noted to you in that Villain your Master, hath now broke forth in a manifest Fact. I was proceeding to my Neighbour *Spruce*'s Church, where I purposed to preach a Funeral Sermon, on the Death of Mr. *John Gage,* the Exciseman; when I was met by two Persons who are, it seems, Sheriffs Officers, and arrested for the 150*l.* which your Master had lent me; and unless I can find Bail within these few Days, of which I see no likelihood, I shall be carried to Goal. This accounts for my not having visited you these two Days; which you might assure yourself, I should not have fail'd, if the *Potestas* had not been wanting. If you can by any means prevail on your Master to release me, I beseech you so to do, not scrupling any thing for Righteousness sake. I hear he is just arrived in this Country, I have herewith sent him a Letter, of which I transmit you a Copy. So with Prayers for your Success, I subscribe myself

Your affectionate Friend,

ARTHUR WILLIAMS.

Parson WILLIAMS *to Squire* BOOBY.

Honoured Sir,

I AM justly surprized to feel so heavy a Weight of your Displeasure, without being conscious of the least Demerit towards so good and generous a Patron, as I have ever found you: For my own Part, I can truly say,

Nil conscire sibi nullæ pallescere culpæ.

And therefore, as this Proceeding is so contrary to your usual Goodness, which I have often experienced, and more especially in the Loan of this Money for which I am now arrested; I cannot avoid thinking some malicious Persons have insinuated false Suggestions against me; intending thereby, to eradicate those Seeds of Affection which I have hardly travailed to sowe in your Heart, and which promised to produce such excellent Fruit. If I have any ways offended you, Sir, be graciously pleased to let me know it, and likewise to point out to me, the Means whereby I may reinstate myself in your Favour: For next to him, whom the Great themselves must bow down before, I know none to whom I shall bend with more Lowliness than your Honour. Permit me to subscribe myself,

Honoured Sir,

Your most obedient, and most obliged,

And most dutiful humble Servant,

ARTHUR WILLIAMS.

The Fate of poor Mr. *Williams* shocked me more than my own: For, as the *Beggar's Opera* says, *Nothing moves one so much as a great Man in Distress.* And to see a Man of his Learning forced to submit so low, to one whom I have often heard him say, he despises, is, I think, a most affecting Circumstance. I write all this to you, Dear Mamma, at the Inn where I lie this first Night, and as I shall send it immediately, by the Post, it will be in Town a little before me.——Don't let my coming away vex you: For, as my Master will be in Town in a few Days, I shall have an Opportunity of seeing him; and let the worst come to the worst, I shall be sure of my Settlement at last. Which is all, from

Your dutiful Daughter,

SHAMELA.

P.S. Just as I was going to send this away a Letter is come from my Master, desiring me to return, with a large Number of Promises.—I have him now as sure as a Gun, as you will perceive by the Letter itself, which I have inclosed to you.

This Letter is unhappily lost, as well as the next which *Shamela* wrote, and which contained an Account of all the Proceedings previous to her Marriage. The only remaining one which I could preserve, seems to have been written about a Week after the Ceremony was perform'd, and is as follows:

Shamela Booby *to* Henrietta Maria Honora Andrews.

Madam,

In my last I left off at our sitting down to Supper on our Wedding Night,* where I behaved with as much Bashfulness as the purest Virgin in the World could have done. The most difficult Task for me was to blush; however, by holding my Breath, and squeezing my Cheeks with my Handkerchief, I did pretty well. My Husband was extreamly eager and impatient to have Supper removed, after which he gave me leave to retire into my Closet for a Quarter of an Hour, which was very agreeable to me; for I employed that time in writing to Mr. *Williams,* who, as I informed you in my last, is released, and presented to the Living, upon the Death of the last Parson. Well, at last I went to Bed, and my Husband soon leapt in after me; where I shall only assure you, I acted my Part

* This was the Letter which is lost.

in such a manner, that no Bridegroom was ever better satisfied with his Bride's Virginity. And to confess the Truth, I might have been well enough satisfied too, if I had never been acquainted with Parson *Williams.*

O what regard Men who marry Widows should have to the Qualifications of their former Husbands.

We did not rise the next Morning till eleven, and then we sat down to Breakfast; I eat two Slices of Bread and Butter, and drank three Dishes of Tea, with a good deal of Sugar, and we both look'd very silly. After Breakfast we drest our selves, he in a blue Camblet Coat, very richly lac'd, and Breeches of the same; with a Paduasoy Waistcoat, laced with Silver; and I, in one of my Mistress's Gowns. I will have finer when I come to Town. We then took a Walk in the Garden, and he kissed me several Times, and made me a Present of 100 Guineas, which I gave away before Night to the Servants, twenty to one, and ten to another, and so on.

We eat a very hearty Dinner, and about eight in the Evening went to Bed again. He is prodigiously fond of me; but I don't like him half so well as my dear *Williams.* The next Morning we rose earlier, and I asked him for another hundred Guineas, and he gave them me. I sent fifty to Parson *Williams,* and the rest I gave away, two Guineas to a Beggar, and three to a Man riding along the Road, and the rest to other People. I long to be in *London* that I may have an Opportunity of laying some out, as well as giving away. I believe I shall buy every Thing I see. What signifies having Money if one doth not spend it.

The next Day, as soon as I was up, I asked him for another Hundred. Why, my Dear, says he, I don't grudge you any thing, but how was it possible for you to lay out the other two Hundred here. La! Sir, says I, I hope I am not obliged to give you an Account of every Shilling; Troth, that will be being your Servant still. I assure you, I married you with no such view, besides did not you tell me I should be Mistress of your Estate? And I will be too. For tho' I brought no Fortune, I am as much your Wife as if I had brought a Million—yes, but, my Dear, says he, if you had brought a Million, you would spend it all at this rate; besides, what will your Expences be in *London,* if they are so great here. Truly, says I, Sir, I shall live like other Ladies of my Fashion; and if you think, because I was a Servant, that I shall be contented to be governed as you please, I will shew you, you are mistaken. If you had not cared to marry me, you might have let it alone. I did not ask you, nor I did not court you. Madam, says he, I don't value a hundred

Guineas to oblige you; but this is a Spirit which I did not expect in you, nor did I ever see any Symptoms of it before. O but Times are altered now, I am your Lady, Sir; yes to my Sorrow, says he, I am afraid—and I am afraid to my Sorrow too: For if you begin to use me in this manner already, I reckon you will beat me before a Month's at an End. I am sure if you did, it would injure me less than this barbarous Treatment; upon which I burst into Tears, and pretended to fall into a Fit. This frighted him out of his wits, and he called up the Servants. Mrs. *Jewkes* immediately came in, and she and another of the Maids fell heartily to rubbing my Temples, and holding Smelling-Bottles to my Nose. Mrs. *Jewkes* told him she fear'd I should never recover, upon which he began to beat his Breasts, and cried out, O my dearest Angel, curse on my passionate Temper, I have destroy'd her, I have destroy'd her!—would she had spent my whole Estate rather than this had happened. Speak to me, my Love, I will melt myself into Gold for thy Pleasure. At last having pretty well tired my self with counterfeiting, and imagining I had continu'd long enough for my purpose in the sham Fit, I began to move my Eyes, to loosen my Teeth, and to open my Hands, which Mr. *Booby* no sooner perceived then he embraced and kissed me with the eagerest

Extacy, asked my Pardon on his Knees for what I had suffered through his Folly and Perverseness, and without more Questions fetched me the Money. I fancy I have effectually prevented any further Refusals or Inquiry into my Expences. It would be hard indeed, that a Woman who marries a Man only for his Money, should be debarred from spending it.

Well, after all Things were quiet, we sat down to Breakfast, yet I resolved not to smile once, nor to say one good-natured, or good-humoured Word on any Account.

Nothing can be more prudent in a Wife, than a sullen Backwardness to Reconciliation; it makes a Husband fearful of offending by the Length of his Punishment.

When we were drest, the Coach was by my Desire ordered for an Airing, which we took in it. A long Silence prevailed on both Sides, tho' he constantly squeezed my Hand, and kissed me, and used other Familiarities, which I peevishly permitted. At last, I opened my Mouth first.—And so, says I, you are sorry you are married?—Pray, my Dear, says he, forget what I said in a Passion. Passion, says I, is apter to discover our Thoughts than to teach us to counterfeit. Well, says he, whether you will believe me or no, I solemnly vow, I would not change thee for the richest Woman in the Universe. No, I warrant you, says I; and yet you could refuse me a nasty hundred Pound. At these very Words, I saw Mr. *Williams* riding as fast as he could across a Field; and I looked out, and saw a Lease of Greyhounds coursing a Hare, which they presently killed, and I saw him alight, and take it from them.

My Husband ordered *Robin* to drive towards him, and looked horribly out of Humour, which I presently imputed to Jealousy. So I began with him first; for that is the wisest way. La, Sir, says I; what makes you look so Angry and Grim? Doth the Sight of Mr. *Williams* give you all this Uneasiness? I am sure, I would never have married a Woman of whom I had so bad an Opinion, that I must be uneasy at every Fellow she looks at. My Dear, answered he, you injure me extremely, you was not in my Thoughts, nor, indeed, could be, while they were covered by so morose a Countenance; I am justly angry with that Parson, whose Family hath been raised from the Dunghill by ours; and who hath received from me twenty Kindnesses, and yet is not contented to destroy the Game in all other Places, which I freely give him leave to do; but hath the Impudence to pursue a few Hares, which I am desirous to preserve, round about this little Coppice. Look, my Dear, pray look, says he; I believe he is going to turn Higler. To confess the Truth, he had no less than three ty'd up behind his Horse, and a fourth he held in his Hand.

Pshaw, says I, I wish all the Hares in the Country were d———d (the Parson himself chid me afterwards for using the Word, tho' it was in his Service.) Here's a Fuss, indeed, about a nasty little pitiful Creature, that is not half so useful as a Cat. You shall not persuade me, that a Man of your Understanding, would quarrel with a Clergyman for such a Trifle. No, no, I am the Hare, for whom poor Parson *Williams* is persecuted; and Jealousy is the Motive. If you had married one of your Quality Ladies, she would have had Lovers by dozens, she would so; but because you have taken a Servant-Maid, forsooth! You are jealous if she but looks (and then I began to Water) at a poor P—a—a—rson in his Pu—u—u—lpit, and then out burst a Flood of Tears.

My Dear, said he, for Heaven's sake dry your Eyes, and don't let him be a Witness of your Tears, which I should be sorry to think might be imputed to my Unkindness; I have already given you some Proofs that I am not jealous of this Parson; I will now give you a very strong One: For I will mount my Horse, and you shall take *Williams* into the Coach. You may be sure, this Motion pleased me, yet I pretended to make as light of it as possible, and told him, I was sorry his Behaviour had made some such glaring Instance, necessary to the perfect clearing my Character.

He soon came up to Mr. *Williams,* who had attempted to ride off, but was prevented by one of our Horsemen, whom my Husband sent to stop him. When we met, my Husband asked him how he did with a very good-humoured Air, and told him he perceived he had found good Sport that Morning. He answered pretty moderate, Sir; for that he had found the three Hares tied on to the Saddle dead in a Ditch (winking on me at the same Time) and added he was sorry there was such a Rot among them.

Well, says Mr. *Booby,* if you please, Mr. *Williams,* you shall come in and ride with my Wife. For my own part, I will mount on Horseback; for it is fine Weather, and besides, it doth not become me to loll in a Chariot, whilst a Clergyman rides on Horseback.

At which Words, Mr. *Booby* leapt out, and Mr. *Williams* leapt in, in an Instant, telling my Husband as he mounted, he was glad to see such a Reformation, and that if he continued his Respect to the Clergy, he might assure himself of Blessings from above.

It was now that the Airing began to grow pleasant to me. Mr. *Williams,* who never had but one Fault, *viz.* that he generally smells of Tobacco, was now perfectly sweet; for he had for two Days together enjoined himself as a Penance, not to smoke till he had kissed my Lips. I will loosen you from that Obligation, says I, and observing my Husband looking another way, I gave him a charming Kiss, and then he asked me Questions concerning my Wedding-night; this actually made me blush: I vow I did not think it had been in him.

As he went along, he began to discourse very learnedly, and told me the Flesh and the Spirit were two distinct Matters, which had not the least relation to each other. That all immaterial Substances (those were his very Words) such as Love, Desire, and so forth, were guided by the Spirit: But fine Houses, large Estates, Coaches, and dainty Entertainments were the Product of the Flesh. Therefore, says he, my Dear, you have two Husbands, one the Object of your Love, and to satisfy your Desire; the other the Object of your Necessity, and to furnish you with those other Conveniencies. (I am sure I remember every Word, for he repeated it three Times; O he is very good whenever I desire him to repeat a thing to me three times he always doth it!) as then the Spirit is preferable to the

Flesh, so am I preferable to your other Husband, to whom I am antecedent in Time likewise. I say these things, my Dear, (said he) to satisfie your Conscience. A Fig for my Conscience, said I, when shall I meet you again in the Garden?

My Husband now rode up to the Chariot, and asked us how we did—I hate the Sight of him. Mr. *Williams* answered very well, at your Service. They then talked of the Weather, and other things, I wished him gone again, every Minute; but all in vain, I had no more Opportunity of conversing with Mr. *Williams*.

Well; at Dinner Mr. *Booby* was very civil to Mr. *Williams,* and told him he has sorry for what had happened, and would make him sufficient Amends, if in his power, and desired him to accept of a Note for fifty Pounds; which he was so *good* to receive, notwithstanding all that had past; and told Mr. *Booby,* he hop'd he would be forgiven, and that he would pray for him.

We make a charming Fool of him, i'fackins; Times are finely altered, I have entirely got the better of him, and am resolved never to give him his Humour.

O how foolish it is in a Woman, who hath once got the Reins into her own Hand, ever to quit them again.

After Dinner Mr. *Williams* drank the Church *et cætera;* and smiled on me; when my Husband's Turn came, he drank *et cætera* and the Church; for which he was very severely rebuked by Mr. *Williams;* it being a high Crime, it seems, to name any thing before the Church. I do not know what *Et cetera* is, but I believe it is something concerning chusing Pallament Men; for I asked if it was not a Health to Mr. *Booby's* Borough, and Mr. *Williams* with a hearty Laugh answered, Yes, Yes, it is his Borough we mean.

I slipt out as soon as I could, hoping Mr. *Williams* would finish the Squire, as I have heard him say he could easily do, and come to me; but it happened quite otherwise, for in about half an Hour, *Booby* came to me, and told me he had left Mr. *Williams,* the Mayor of his Borough, and two or three Aldermen heartily at it, and asked me if I would go hear *Williams* sing a Catch, which, added he, he doth to a Miracle.

Every Opportunity of seeing my dear *Williams,* was agreeable to me, which indeed I scarce had at this Time; for when we returned, the whole Corporation were got together, and the Room was in a Cloud of Tobacco; Parson *Williams* was at the upper End of the Table, and he hath pure round cherry Cheeks, and his Face look'd all the World to nothing like the Sun in a Fog. If the Sun had a Pipe in his Mouth, there would be no Difference.

I began now to grow uneasy, apprehending I should have no more of Mr. *Williams's* Company that Evening, and not at all caring for my Husband, I advised him to sit down and drink for his Country with the rest of the Company; but he refused, and desired me to give him some Tea; swearing nothing made him so sick, as to hear a Parcel of Scoundrels roaring forth the Principles of honest Men over their Cups, when, says he, I know most of them are such empty Blockheads, that they don't know their right Hand from their left; and that Fellow there, who hath talked so much of *Shipping,* at the left Side of the Parson, in whom they all place a Confidence, if I don't take care, will sell them to my Adversary.

I don't know why I mention this Stuff to you; for I am sure I know nothing about *Pollitricks,* more than Parson *Williams* tells me, who says that the Court-side are in the right on't, and that every Christian ought to be on the same with the Bishops.

When we had finished our Tea, we walked in the Garden till it was dark, and then my Husband proposed, instead of returning to the Company, (which I desired, that I might see Parson *Williams* again,) to sup in another Room by our selves, which,

for fear of making him jealous, and considering too, that Parson *Williams* would be pretty far gone, I was obliged to consent to.

O! what a devilish Thing it is, for a Woman to be obliged to go to Bed to a spindle-shanked young Squire, she doth not like, when there is a jolly Parson in the same House she is fond of.

In the Morning I grew very peevish, and in the Dumps, notwithstanding all he could say or do to please me. I exclaimed against the Priviledge of Husbands, and vowed I would not be pulled and tumbled about. At last he hit on the only Method, which could have brought me into Humour, and proposed to me a Journey to *London,* within a few Days. This you may easily guess pleased me; for besides the Desire which I have of shewing my self forth, of buying fine Cloaths, Jewels, Coaches, Houses, and ten thousand other fine Things, Parson *Williams* is, it seems, going thither too, to be *instuted.*

O! what a charming Journey I shall have; for I hope to keep the dear Man in the Chariot with me all the way; and that foolish Booby (for that is the Name Mr. Williams *hath set him) will ride on Horseback.*

So as I shall have an Opportunity of seeing you so shortly, I think I will mention no more Matters to you now. O I had like to have forgot one very material Thing; which is that it will look horribly, for a Lady of my Quality and Fashion, to own such a Woman as you for my Mother. Therefore we must meet in private only, and if you will never claim me, nor mention me to any one, I will always allow you what is very handsome. Parson *Williams* hath greatly advised me in this, and says, he thinks I should do very well to lay out twenty Pounds, and set you up in a little Chandler's Shop: but you must remember all my Favours to you will depend on your Secrecy; for I am positively resolved, I will not be known to be your Daughter; and if you tell any one so, I shall deny it with all my Might, which Parson *Williams* says, I may do with a safe Conscience, being now a married Woman. So I rest

Your humble Servant

SHAMELA.

P. S. The strangest Fancy hath enter'd into my *Booby's* Head, that can be imagined. He is resolved to have a Book made about him and me; he proposed it to Mr. *Williams,* and offered him a Reward for his Pains; but he says he never writ any thing of that kind, but will recommend my Husband, when he comes to Town, to a Parson *who does that Sort of Business for Folks,* one who can make my Husband, and me, and Parson *Williams,* to be all great People; for he *can make black white,* it seems. Well, but they say my Name is to be altered, Mr. *Williams,* says the first Syllabub hath too comical a Sound, so it is to be changed into *Pamela;* I own I can't imagine what can be said; for to be sure I shan't confess any of my Secrets to them, and so I whispered Parson *Williams* about that, who answered me, I need not give my self any Trouble: for the Gentleman *who writes Lives,* never asked more than a few Names of his Customers, and that he made all the rest out of his own Head; you mistake, Child, said he, if you apprehend any Truths are to be delivered. So far on the contrary, if you had not been acquainted with the Name, you would not have known it to be your own History. I have seen a *Piece of his Performance,* where the Person, whose Life was written, could he have risen from the Dead again, would not have even suspected he had been aimed at, unless by the Title of the Book, which was superscribed with his Name. Well, all these Matters are strange to me, yet I can't help laughing, to think I shall see my self in a printed Book.

So much for Mrs. *Shamela,* or *Pamela,* which I have taken Pains to transcribe from the Originals, sent down by her Mother in a Rage, at the Proposal in her last Letter. The Originals themselves are in my Hands, and shall be communicated to you, if you think proper to make them publick; and certainly they will have their Use. The Character of *Shamela,* will make young Gentlemen wary how they take the most fatal Step both to themselves and Families, by youthful, hasty and improper Matches; indeed, they may assure themselves, that all such Prospects of Happiness are vain and delusive, and that they sacrifice all the solid Comforts of their Lives, to a very transient Satisfaction of a Passion, which how hot so ever it be, will be soon cooled; and when cooled, will afford them nothing but Repentance.

Can any thing be more miserable, than to be despised by the whole World, and that must certainly be the Consequence; to be despised by the Person obliged, which it is more than probable will be the Consequence, and of which, we see an Instance in *Shamela;* and lastly to despise one's self, which must be the Result of any Reflection on so weak and unworthy a Choice.

As to the Character of Parson *Williams,* I am sorry it is a true one. Indeed those who do not know him, will hardly believe it so; but what Scandal doth it throw on the Order to have one bad Member, unless they endeavour to screen and protect him? In him you see a Picture of almost every Vice exposed in nauseous and odious Colours; and if a Clergyman would ask me by what Pattern he should form himself, I would say, Be the reverse of *Williams:* So far therefore he may be of use to the Clergy themselves, and though God forbid there should be many *Williams's* amongst them, you and I are too honest to pretend, that the Body wants no Reformation.

To say the Truth, I think no greater Instance of the contrary can be given than that which appears in your Letter. The confederating to cry up a nonsensical ridiculous Book, (I believe the most extensively so of any ever yet published,) and to be so weak and so wicked as to pretend to make it a Matter of Religion; whereas so far from having any moral Tendency, the Book is by no means innocent: For,

First, There are many lascivious Images in it, very improper to be laid before the Youth of either Sex.

2dly, Young Gentlemen are here taught, that to marry their Mother's Chambermaids, and to indulge the Passion of Lust, at the Expence of Reason and Common Sense, is an Act of Religion, Virtue, and Honour; and, indeed the surest Road to Happiness.

3dly, All Chambermaids are strictly enjoyned to look out after their Masters; they are taught to use little Arts to that purpose: And lastly, are countenanced in Impertinence to their Superiours, and in betraying the Secrets of Families.

4thly, In the Character of Mrs. *Jewkes* Vice is rewarded; whence every Housekeeper may learn the Usefulness of pimping and bawding for her Master.

5thly, In Parson *Williams,* who is represented as a faultless Character, we see a busy Fellow, intermeddling with the private Affairs of his Patron, whom he is very ungratefully forward to expose and condemn on every Occasion.

Many more Objections might, if I had Time or Inclination, be made to this Book; but I apprehend, what hath been said is sufficient to perswade you of the use which may arise from publishing an Antidote to this Poison. I have therefore sent you the Copies of these Papers, and if you have Leisure to communicate them to the Press, I will transmit you the Originals, tho' I assure you, the Copies are exact.

I shall only add, that there is not the least Foundation for any thing which is said of Lady *Davers,* or any of the other Ladies; all that is merely to be imputed to the Invention of the Biographer. I have particularly enquired after Lady *Davers,* and don't hear Mr. *Booby* hath such a Relation, or that there is indeed any such Person existing. I am,

Dear Sir,

Most faithfully and respectfully,

Your humble Servant,

J. OLIVER.

Parson TICKLETEXT *to Parson* OLIVER.

Dear SIR,

I HAVE read over the History of *Shamela,* as it appears in those authentick Copies you favour me with, and am very much ashamed of the Character, which I was hastily prevailed on to give that Book. I am equally angry with the pert Jade herself, and with the Author of her Life: For I scarce know yet to whom I chiefly owe an Imposition, which hath been so general, that if Numbers could defend me from Shame, I should have no Reason to apprehend it.

As I have your implied Leave to publish, what you so kindly sent me, I shall not wait for the Originals, as you assure me the Copies are exact, and as I am really impatient to do what I think a serviceable Act of Justice to the World.

Finding by the End of her last Letter, that the little Hussy was in Town, I made it pretty much my Business to enquire after her, but with no effect hitherto: As soon as I succeed in this Enquiry, you shall hear what Discoveries I can learn. You will pardon the Shortness of this Letter, as you shall be troubled with a much longer very soon: And believe me,

Dear Sir,

Your most faithful Servant,

THO. TICKLETEXT.

P. S. Since I write, I have a certain Account, that Mr. *Booby* hath caught his Wife in bed with *Williams;* hath turned her off, and is prosecuting him in the spiritual Court.

FINIS.

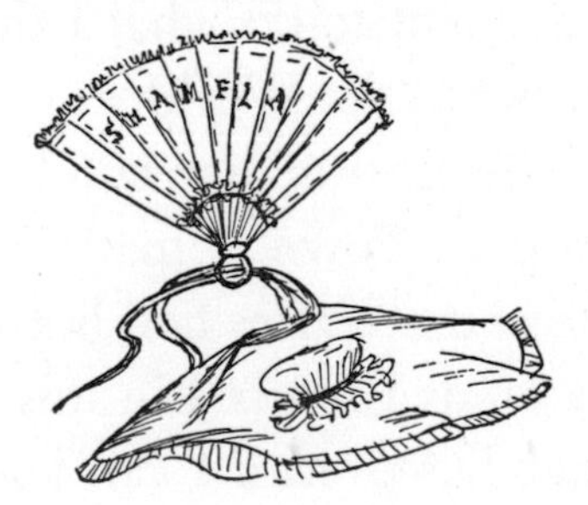